RIFF BY RIFF:
PAUL WELLER

Wise Publications
London/New York/Sydney/Paris/Copenhagen/Madrid
www.musicinprint.com

Exclusive Distributors:
Music Sales Limited
8/9 Frith Street,
London W1V 5TZ, England.
Music Sales Pty Limited
120 Rothschild Avenue
Rosebery, NSW 2018,
Australia.

Order No. AM944230
ISBN 0-7119-6604-4
This book © Copyright 1999 by Wise Publications

Music arranged by Martin Shellard
Additional text and editing by Derek Jones
All recording and guitars by Martin Shellard
Music processed by Paul Ewers Music Design
Cover design by Johnson Banks
Photographs courtesy of London Features International

Printed in Great Britain by
Printwise (Haverhill) Limited, Suffolk.

Your Guarantee of Quality
As publishers, we strive to produce every book to the highest commercial standards.
The book has been carefully designed to minimise awkward page turns and to make playing from it a real pleasure.
Particular care has been given to specifying acid-free, neutral-sized paper
made from pulps which have not been elemental chlorine bleached.
This pulp is from farmed sustainable forests and was produced with special regard for the environment.
Throughout, the printing and binding have been planned to ensure a sturdy,
attractive publication which should give years of enjoyment.
If your copy fails to meet our high standards, please inform us and we will gladly replace it.

Music Sales' complete catalogue describes thousands of titles
and is available in full colour sections by subject, direct from Music Sales Limited.
Please state your areas of interest and send a cheque/postal order for £1.50 for postage to:
Music Sales Limited, Newmarket Road, Bury St. Edmunds, Suffolk IP33 3YB.

CONTENTS

	Page	CD Tracks
Introduction	5	
Tab Guide	6	
ALL THE PICTURES ON THE WALL		
The Riffs	8	1-7
Riff Route Map	12	8-9
Lyrics	13	
INTO TOMORROW		
The Riffs	15	10-15
Riff Route Map	18	16-17
Lyrics	19	
OUT OF THE SINKING		
The Riffs	20	18-33
Riff Route Map	26	34-35
Lyrics	27	
PEACOCK SUIT		
The Riffs	28	36-44
Riff Route Map	32	45-46
Lyrics	33	
SUNFLOWER		
The Riffs	35	47-52
Riff Route Map	38	53-54
Lyrics	39	
THE CHANGINGMAN		
The Riffs	40	55-59
Riff Route Map	42	60-61
Lyrics	43	
WOODCUTTER'S SON		
The Riffs	44	62-65
Riff Route Map	46	66-67
Lyrics	47	

"I mainly just like listening to mu...
still inspires me - I still get some...
from it, a very personal thing I ca...
into words. It's the only thing that...
excites me, to be honest. It worri...
sometimes, because it does feel lik...
got a very one-dimensional life. It a...
seems to revolve around musi...
that's the way it is, I've accept...

RIFF BY RIFF...PAUL WELLER

Learning Is Easy When You Know How!

How often do you see a guitarist in a band - amateur or professional - using sheet music?

Very rarely, if ever at all! So how do they remember all those songs, with so many different notes, phrases and solos?

Simple - by breaking each song down into manageable, easy to learn chunks, typically eight bars or so long. You are probably already familiar with the names given to these sections - verse, chorus, bridge, middle eight, and so on.

Each of these sections is made up of smaller passages or 'building blocks' - these are known as riffs.

That's what this book is all about - learning to play a song bit by bit using these building blocks or riffs, then putting them together in the correct order.

It's All In The Riffs!

You will immediately begin learning songs by playing the individual riffs that make up each song. These fall into two types - 'riffs' and 'rhythm riffs'.

Riffs are short, melodic phrases, usually repeated a number of times throughout a song. Riffs are often a song's most instantly recognisable trademark - the seven note riff that kicks off 'Layla', for example - so mastering them is essential.

Rhythm riffs are chord-based patterns that underpin the structure of a song and can be just as crucial. A good example would be the underlining rhythm riffs that propel each verse of the classic 'Sultans Of Swing'.

Each riff is notated in both standard and tab notation, while the rhythm riffs appear as guitar chord boxes with the relevant rhythms below.

The riffs are presented in the order in which they appear in the song and each one comes with an explanation, offering help on how to play it. Listen to the relevant track number on the CD for a demonstration of how each riff should sound.

The Route To Success

Once you have got to grips with all the riffs of a song, it's time to link them all together using the second section - the 'Riff Route Map'.

This clearly displays the structure of each song, showing you exactly where to play each of the riffs you have learned. These maps are also collected together in a special pull-out section for ease of use. There are handy markers to help keep you on track, such as lyric cues and timing boxes, which relate directly to the music on the CD.

Now here's the good part - as well as featuring audio examples of how every riff should sound in isolation, the CD also contains full-length song demonstrations and complete backing tracks for you to practice your riffs to, play each guitar part or simply to jam along with! When used in conjunction with these audio tracks, the Riff Route Map makes it clear exactly how all the different elements of the song are brought together.

Following each Riff Route Map is a complete lyric guide with guitar boxes and chord symbols, presenting a quick and useful one-page reference to all the lyrics and chord changes for each song.

Are You Ready To Play?

Each book in the 'Riff By Riff' series not only teaches you the essential riffs from the greatest songs by some of the world's finest guitarists and bands, it also gives you an inside look at the techniques, skills and secrets of each player.

With authentic tablature transcriptions, CD demonstrations and backing tracks, notes on how to play each riff, in-depth technique advice and guidance on how to get the right sound, 'Riff By Riff' gives you a complete and thorough breakdown of how to play in the style of your favourite guitarist.

Now that's the introduction dispensed with, get ready to riff!

Guitar Tablature Explained

Guitar music can be notated three different ways: on a musical stave, in tablature, and in rhythm slashes

RHYTHM SLASHES are written above the stave. Strum chords in the rhythm indicated. Round noteheads indicate single notes.

THE MUSICAL STAVE shows pitches and rhythms and is divided by lines into bars. Pitches are named after the first seven letters of the alphabet.

TABLATURE graphically represents the guitar fingerboard. Each horizontal line represents a string, and each number represents a fret.

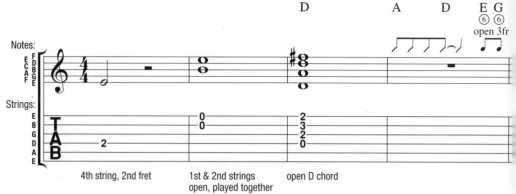

4th string, 2nd fret

1st & 2nd strings open, played together

open D chord

definitions for special guitar notation

SEMI-TONE BEND: Strike the note and bend up a semi-tone (1/2 step).

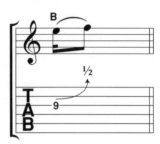

WHOLE-TONE BEND: Strike the note and bend up a whole-tone (whole step).

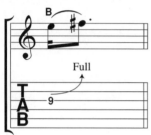

GRACE NOTE BEND: Strike the note and bend as indicated. Play the first note as quickly as possible.

QUARTER-TONE BEND: Strike the note and bend up a 1/4 step.

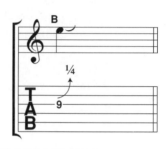

BEND & RELEASE: Strike the note and bend up as indicated, then release back to the original note.

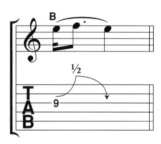

COMPOUND BEND & RELEASE: Strike the note and bend up and down in the rhythm indicated.

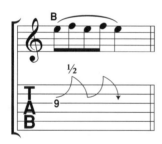

PRE-BEND: Bend the note as indicated, then strike it.

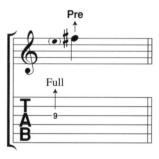

PRE-BEND & RELEASE: Bend the note as indicated. Strike it and release the note back to the original pitch.

UNISON BEND: Strike the two notes simultaneously and bend the lower note up to the pitch of the higher.

BEND & RESTRIKE: Strike the note and bend as indicated then restrike the string where the symbol occurs.

BEND, HOLD AND RELEASE: Same as bend and release but hold the bend for the duration of the tie.

BEND AND TAP: Bend the note as indicated and tap the higher fret while still holding the bend.

VIBRATO: The string is vibrated by rapidly bending and releasing the note with the fretting hand.

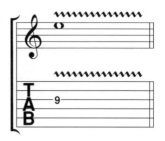

HAMMER-ON: Strike the first (lower) note with one finger, then sound the higher note (on the same string) with another finger by fretting it without picking.

PULL-OFF: Place both fingers on the notes to be sounded, Strike the first note and without picking, pull the finger off to sound the second (lower) note.

LEGATO SLIDE (GLISS): Strike the first note and then slide the same fret-hand finger up or down to the second note. The second note is not struck.

NOTE: The speed of any bend is indicated by the music notation and tempo.

SHIFT SLIDE (GLISS & RESTRIKE): Same as legato slide, except the second note is struck.

TRILL: Very rapidly alternate between the notes indicated by continuously hammering on and pulling off.

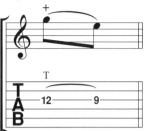

TAPPING: Hammer ("tap") the fret indicated with the pick-hand index or middle finger and pull off to the note fretted by the fret hand.

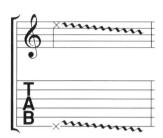

PICK SCRAPE: The edge of the pick is rubbed down (or up) the string, producing a scratchy sound.

MUFFLED STRINGS: A percussive sound is produced by laying the fret hand across the string(s) without depressing, and striking them with the pick hand.

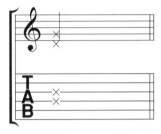

NATURAL HARMONIC: Strike the note while the fret-hand lightly touches the string directly over the fret indicated.

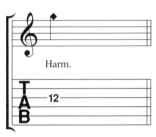

PINCH HARMONIC: The note is fretted normally and a harmonic is produced by adding the edge of the thumb or the tip of the index finger of the pick hand to the normal pick attack.

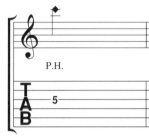

HARP HARMONIC: The note is fretted nor and a harmonic is produced by gently res the pick hand's index finger directly abov indicated fret (in parentheses) while the p hand's thumb or pick assists by plucking appropriate string.

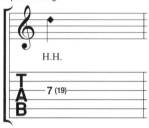

PALM MUTING: The note is partially muted by the pick hand lightly touching the string(s) just before the bridge.

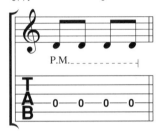

RAKE: Drag the pick across the strings indicated with a single motion.

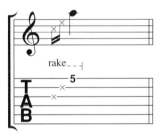

TREMOLO PICKING: The note is picked as rapidly and continuously as possible.

ARPEGGIATE: Play the notes of the chord indicated by quickly rolling them from bottom to top.

SWEEP PICKING: Rhythmic downstroke and/or upstroke motion across the strings.

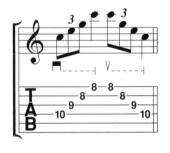

VIBRATO DIVE BAR AND RETURN: The pitch of the note or chord is dropped a specific number of steps (in rhythm) then returned to the original pitch.

VIBRATO BAR SCOOP: Depress the bar just before striking the note, then quickly release the bar.

VIBRATO BAR DIP: Strike the note and then immediately drop a specific number of steps, then release back to the original pitch.

additional musical definitions

(accent) • Accentuate note (play it louder).

(accent) • Accentuate note with great intensity.

(staccato) • Shorten time value of note.

• Downstroke

V • Upstroke

D.%. al Coda

D.C. al Fine

tacet

- Go back to the sign (%), then play un the bar marked *To Coda* ⊕ then skip the section marked ⊕ *Coda*.

- Go back to the beginning of the song play until the bar marked *Fine* (end)

- Instrument is silent (drops out).

- Repeat bars between signs.

- When a repeated section has differer endings, play the first ending only th time and the second ending only the second time.

ALL THE PICTURES ON THE WALL

Words and Music by Paul Weller
© Copyright 1993 Notting Hill Music (UK) Limited,
8B Berkeley Gardens, London W8 4AP.
All Rights Reserved. International Copyright Secured.

The fifth track on the *Wild Wood* album, 'All The Pictures On The Wall' is built around Paul's acoustic guitar playing. The result is a slightly folksy, singer/songwriter atmosphere.

Although made up mainly of rhythm riffs, the song returns insistently to the catchy opening riff, giving a breezy, relaxed feel. When trying to re-create this track, don't stick too rigidly to each pattern – variation and improvisation are important elements in this style of music.

Riff 1

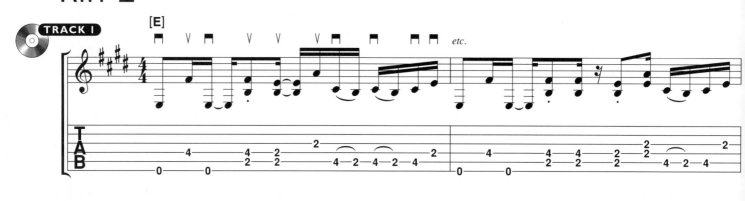

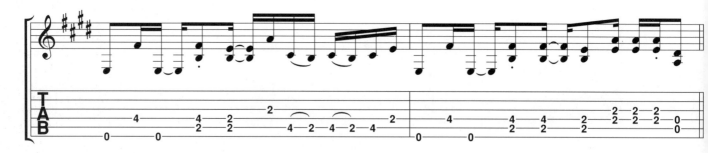

This riff is used as a repeating theme throughout the song and can be heard in the intro, verse and chorus. The riff is never played exactly the same way, so try varying it each time it occurs. Try to keep the bottom string ringing and follow the picking directions – these will help with the feel of the riff.

The main guitar on the recording is an acoustic, but this riff is usually doubled with a clean electric guitar, so it will sound good on either. Use two pickups together on an electric guitar with a clean, bright sound.

Rhythm Riff 1

TRACK 2

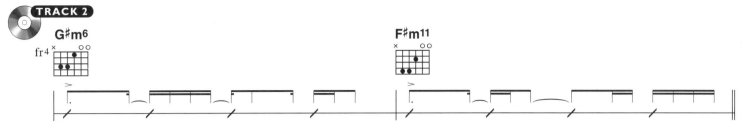

This strumming rhythm pattern is used for the verse. If you look at the chord boxes for this section you'll notice that the top two strings are open for both chords – the moving shape creates the different chords. This is true for most of the rhythm riffs in this song. The accent marks above certain chords show where the whole chord is played, the other chords should be played with only the top three or four strings ringing

Rhythm Riff 2

TRACK 3

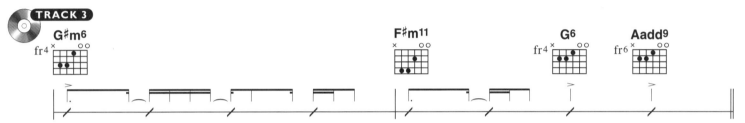

This is very similar to Rhythm Riff 1 except for the two accented chords at the end. This riff is also used in the verse.

"I wouldn't have done anything else. It wasn't even a case of whether I was gonna succeed or not. My success has surpassed anything I ever thought, but I always knew I would just do music, at whatever level I got to."

"The early songs were just straight Beatles rip-offs. We'd get that songbook, 'The Beatles Complete', and go through the chords... so nothing's changed, really!"

Rhythm Riff 3

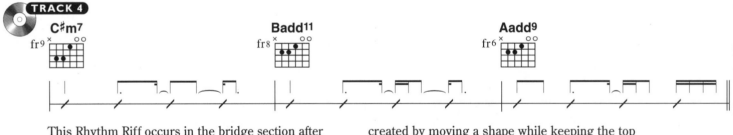

This Rhythm Riff occurs in the bridge section after the first chorus. Once again, different chords are created by moving a shape while keeping the top strings ringing.

Rhythm Riff 4

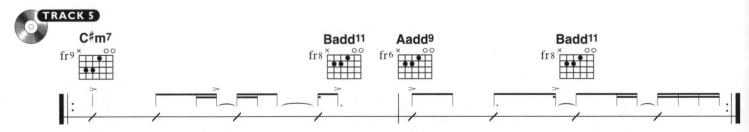

This Riff forms part of the middle 8 and uses the same chords as Rhythm Riff 3 but in a different order. Play full chords where you see the accents and partial chords for the others.

Rhythm Riff 5

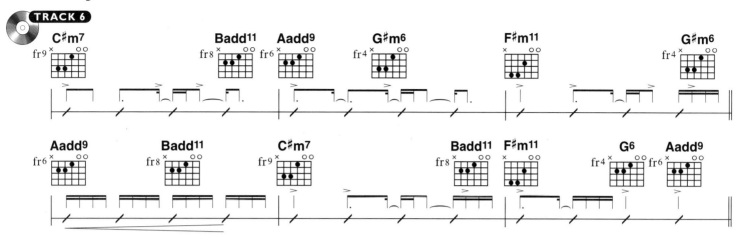

This is a much longer riff which is used for the rest of the middle 8. You'll recognize most of the chords from earlier riffs. Notice the accents on off-beat chords, and watch out for the syncopated chord changes (in the third bar for instance). The Aadd9 and Badd11 chords in the fourth bar should start very quietly and build in volume. You can do this not only by playing softly, but also by playing smaller chords in the quiet part – start by playing the bottom two notes of the first A chord and then gradually increase the number of strings as you build the volume.

Rhythm Riff 6

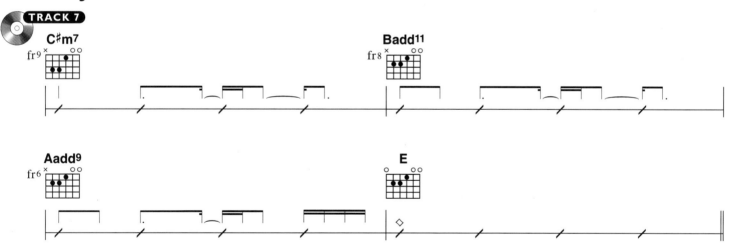

This riff constitutes the coda, and brings the song to a close. It is very similar to Rhythm Riff 3 but with a slightly different strumming pattern and a final E chord.

ALL THE PICTURES ON THE WALL
Riff Route Map

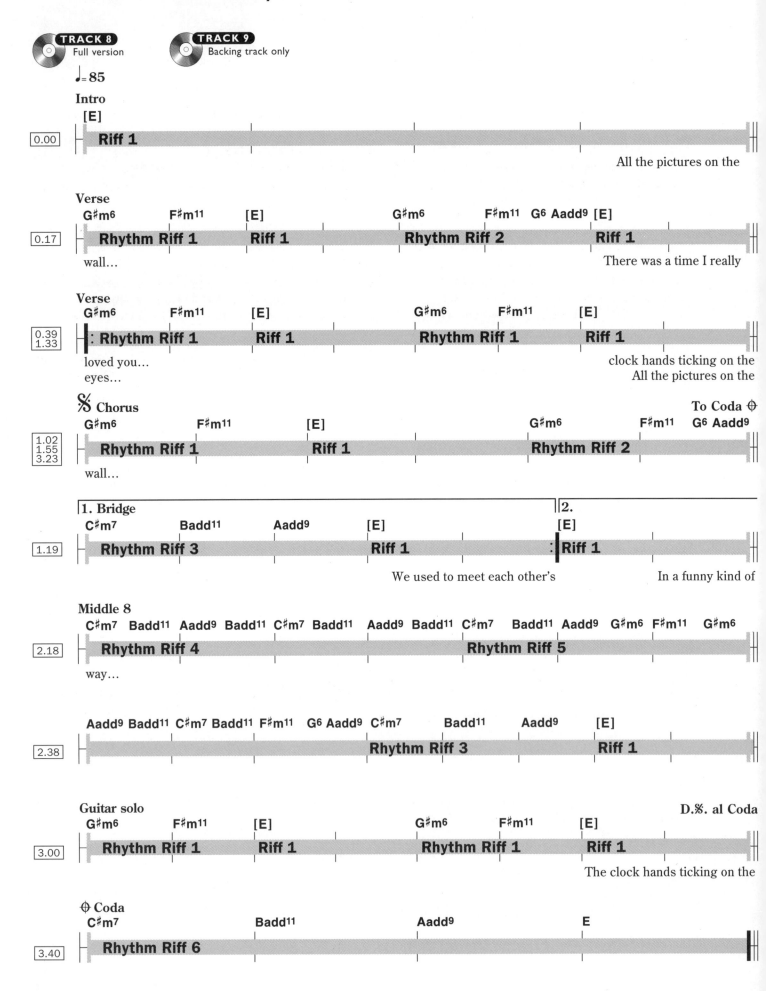

ALL THE PICTURES ON THE WALL
Lyrics

G#m6   F#m11   G6   Aadd9   C#m7   Badd11   E

Intro: (4 bars)

Verse 1:
     [E]   G#m6
And all the pictures on the wall
  F#m11   [E]
Serve only to remind me of it all

                             G#m6
The wasted days we could have lived
  F#m11   G6   Aadd9 [E]
Now we're left with nothing left to give.

Verse 2:
                       G#m6
There was a time I really loved you
  F#m11   [E]
But when that was I just can't say
                   G#m6
As all the memories merge into one
  F#m11   [E]
As each day becomes each day.

Chorus 1:
                     G#m6
The clock hands ticking on the wall
  F#m11   [E]
Are just reminders of it all
                      G#m6
The wasted days we could have lived.

Bridge:
  F#m11   G6   Aadd9   C#m7 Badd11
Now we're left with nothing left to give
           Aadd9 [E]
Nothing left to give.

Verse 3:
                    G#m6
We used to meet each others eyes
  F#m11   [E]
And that's all we'd have to say
                 G#m6
Now we don't talk that much at all
  F#m11   [E]
The further our eyes seem to stray.

Chorus 2:
                      G#m6
And all the pictures on the wall
  F#m11   [E]
Serve only to remind you of it all
                      G#m6
The wasted days we could have lived
  F#m11   G6   Aadd9   [E]
Now we're left with nothing left to give.

Middle 8:
                     C#m7
And in a funny kind of way
  Aadd9   Badd11   C#m7
This empty room was full one day
  Aadd9 Badd11   C#m7 Bsus4
Full of love that we once shared
  Aadd9 G#m6   F#m11   G#m6
Now it looks so bare
  Aadd9   Badd11   C#m7 Badd11
The silent walls whose cracks I feel
    F#m11   G6   Aadd9
But is there room to let the
  C#m7   Badd11 Aadd9
hatred heal.

Gtr. solo: (8 bars)

Chorus 3:
  [E]   G#m6
The clock hands ticking on the wall
  F#m11   [E]
Are just reminders of it all
                      G#m6
The wasted days we could have lived
  F#m11   G6   Aadd9 C#m7
Now we're left with nothing
    Badd11 Aadd9 E
  left to give.

"The turning point for me was writing 'Into Tomorrow' on my first solo album. Up until then I thought I'd lost it. Sometimes you just have to wait until it comes round, which I'm prepared to do now if it happens."

INTO TOMORROW

Words and Music by Paul Weller

Released as a single in 1991, this song features on the album *Paul Weller* and is a great example of Paul's commercial song-writing skill.

The opening riff sounds quirky at first but soon settles into a groove to support the verse. The chorus comes as a release with simple, clean chords underneath some powerful vocals. Weller uses a typical, slightly distorted guitar sound, yet is still able to produce the contrasting moods found within this song.

Riff 1

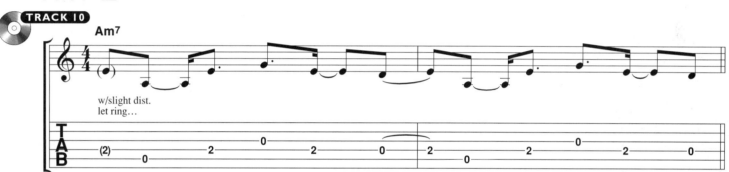

This is a classic jangly Paul Weller riff, reminiscent of the Beatles.

Let all the strings ring out and keep the hammer-ons neat and rhythmic.

Riff 2

This clean-toned, funky riff is used mainly in the verse, but also in combination with Riffs 1 and 3.

Notice how the hammer-ons coincide with the ones in Riff 3. In the second verse, the second bar of this riff is replaced by a single D7sus4 chord (see Rhythm Riff 1 for chord box).

Riff 3

TRACK 12

This riff is a simplified version of Riff 2, and follows
on from Riff 1.

Riff 4

TRACK 13

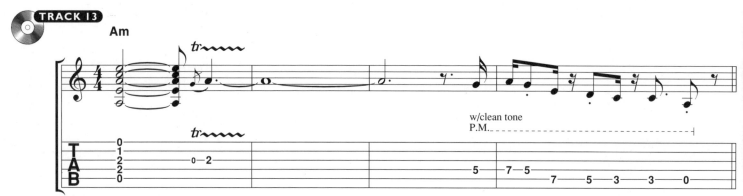

This reggae style riff leads into the guitar solo. Play
the second half of the riff with palm muting.

"Going back and listening to stuff I hadn't listened to for
years, like The Small Faces, re-ignites a certain feeling, and
reminds you what you used to get out of music. It also put
me back in touch with my strengths, with what I'd forgotten
I was good at, which is playing guitar."

"'Into Tomorrow' is... about me trying to get a grip on becoming thirty-something and the great grey mass that lies between the simple black and white world of my youth."

Rhythm Riff 1

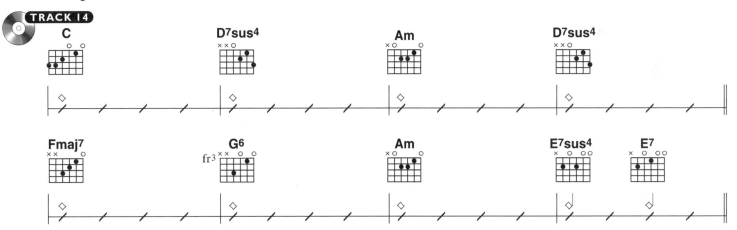

This chord sequence is played under the chorus. Hit the chords hard, making sure they last to the end of the bar.

Rhythm Riff 2

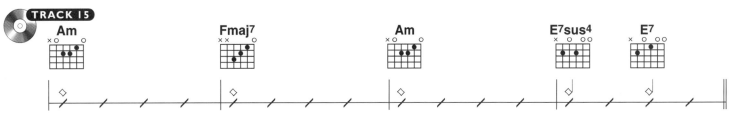

This chord sequence acts as a link from the last chorus to the outro.

INTO TOMORROW
Riff Route Map

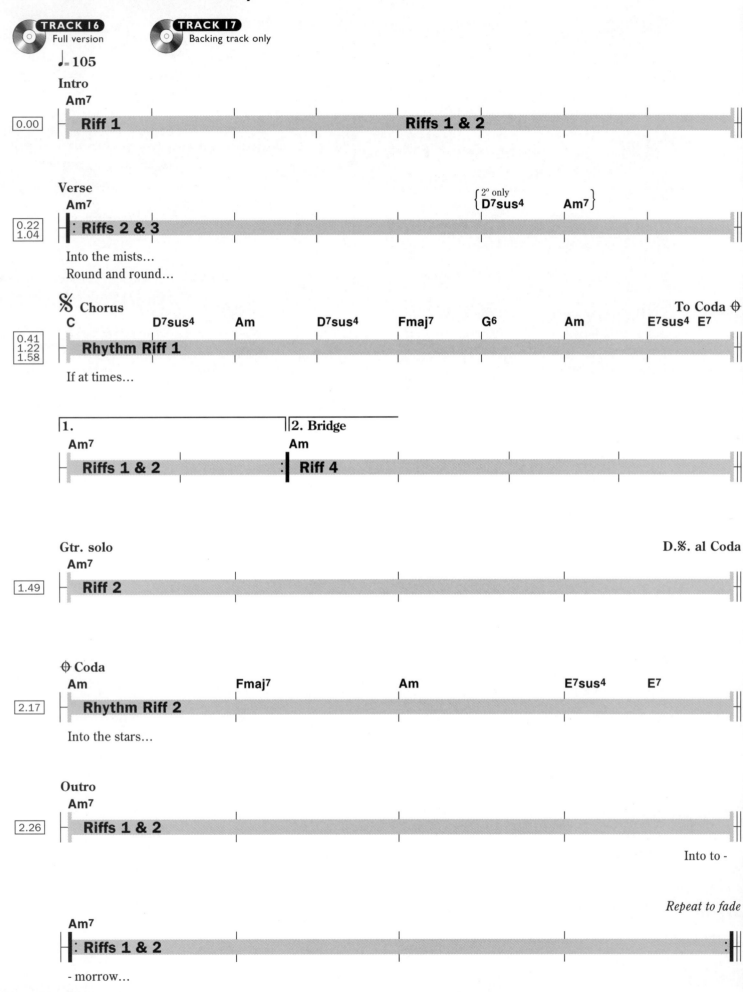

INTO TOMORROW
Lyrics

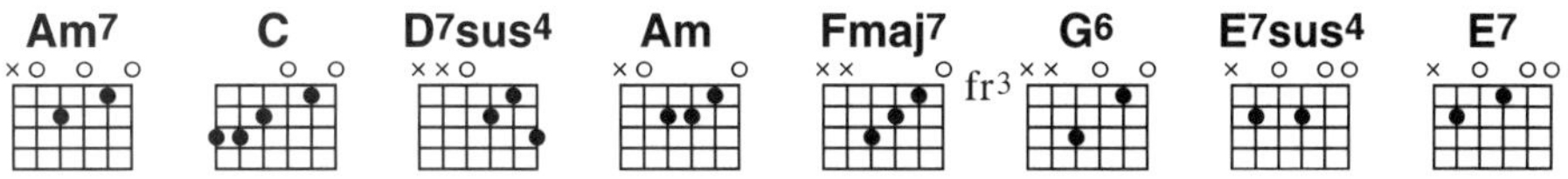

Am⁷ **C** **D⁷sus⁴** **Am** **Fmaj⁷** **G⁶** **E⁷sus⁴** **E⁷**

Intro:
Am⁷
(8 bars)

Verse 1:
Am⁷
Into the mists of time and space
Where we have no say over date
  and place
Don't get embarrassed if it happens
  a lot
That you don't know how you started
  or where you're gonna stop.

Chorus 1:
C   **D⁷sus⁴**
And if at times it seems insane
  – all the tears and searching
Am
Turning all your joy to pain
  D⁷sus⁴
  – in pursuit of learning
Fmaj⁷   **G⁶**
Buy a dream and hideaway
  G⁶
  – can't escape the sorrow
    Am
Your mojo will have no effect
  E⁷sus⁴   **E⁷**
  – as we head into tomorrow.
Am⁷

Verse 2:
Round and round like a twisted wheel
Spinning in attempt to find the feel
Find the path that will help us find
D⁷sus⁴   **Am⁷**
A feeling of control over lives and
  minds.

Chorus 2: (As Chorus 1)
Am   **Am⁷**

Bridge: (4 bars)   (4 bars guitar solo)

Chorus 3: (As Chorus 1)

Coda:
Am
Into the stars and always up
Fmaj⁷
Drinking from a broken cup
Am
Whose golden gleam is fading fast
E⁷sus⁴   **E⁷**   **Am⁷**
Praying that it has not passed.

Fade:
Am⁷
Into tomorrow

OUT OF THE SINKING

Words and Music by Paul Weller
© Copyright 1995 Stylist Music Limited/
BMG Music Publishing Limited, 69/79 Fulham High Street, London SW6.
This arrangement © Copyright 1997 BMG Music Publishing Limited.
All Rights Reserved. International Copyright Secured.

First released as a single in 1994, 'Out Of The Sinking' is track nine on *Stanley Road*. This number can be described as a solid rock song, heavily influenced by the sounds and styles of the early seventies.

Although structurally more complex than most Weller compositions, each element is easy to learn, and piecing them together should be a satisfying experience. One important thing to remember when learning this song is that the tempo is quite slow; this should, with the help of a warm, distorted guitar sound, make for a relaxed and easy feel.

Riff 1a

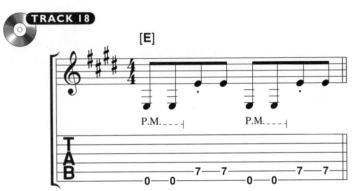

This simple two note riff is used several times throughout the song. The first two notes are played with palm muting, but notice that the next note, although not muted, is played very short. This is important to the feel of the riff. Riff 1b is used toward the end of the song and combines Riff 1a with accented G and A chords which are doubled by the rest of the band. The second bar of Riff 1c builds to a crescendo with the stacatto notes played as normal. The final phrase has a descending line above a ringing bottom E string which raises the energy level into the next section. Use the bridge pickup with a distorted sound.

Riff 1b

Riff 1c

Riff 2

TRACK 21

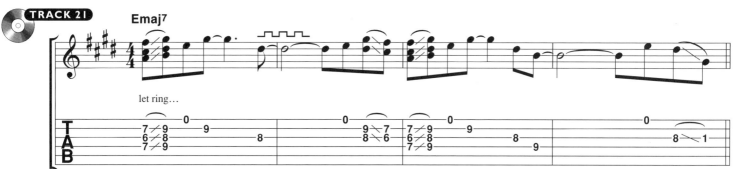

Riff 2 is used in the verses, usually along with Riff 1. Try to keep all strings ringing, especially the top one. The lush major 7 chords help to give this riff a very laid back, relaxed feel.

This riff is played with a lot of variation throughout the song, so feel free to experiment. Use the bridge pickup with a warm, slightly distorted sound

Riff 3

TRACK 22

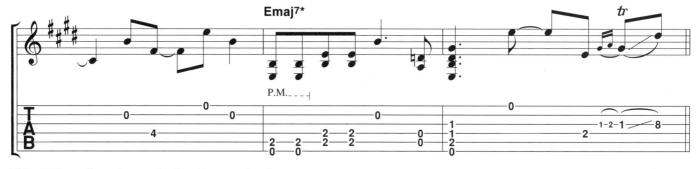

This riff is really an improvised guitar part for the verse. Each verse is different, but based on the same ideas. Use this riff as a basis for improvisation.

Riff 4

TRACK 23

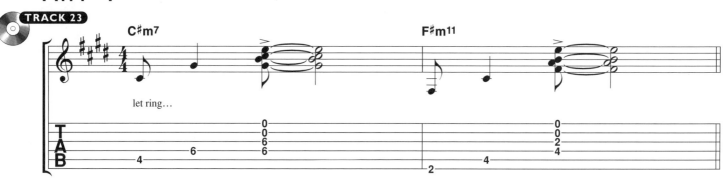

This is the chorus riff. Notice that the top two strings are open for both chords and should be left ringing – this will help smooth out the chord change. (Weller uses a similar technique in 'All The Pictures On The Wall'.) The F#m11 is best played with the fretting hand thumb holding down the bass note. If you're not familiar with this technique it may take a little getting used to. Hold the neck so that your thumb sticks out above the bottom string then curl it over to hold down the note. This is the point where the song takes off so go for a more distorted sound and hit the accents hard.

Riff 5

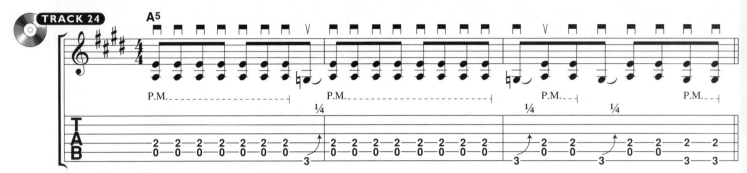

This riff is used to link the chorus with the verse. If you use the strumming directions it will help you get the driving feel of the original. Exaggerate the decorative bend on the bottom string.

Riff 6

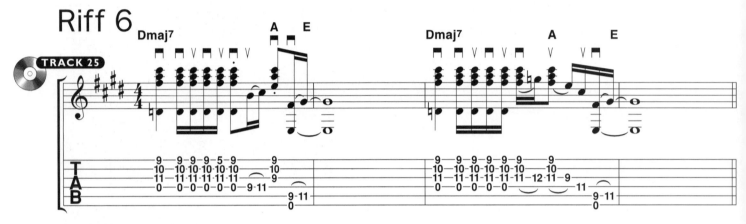

Riff 6 is used for the bridge section. You may find the quick changes between chords and single notes a bit tricky, so practise it slowly and follow the picking directions. Use your first finger to barre the top three strings and use a full distorted sound. The last two bars of this riff are used to finish off the song.

"I wanted to write a great English mod love song and 'Out Of The Sinking' is it. It still makes my back tingle when I hear it."

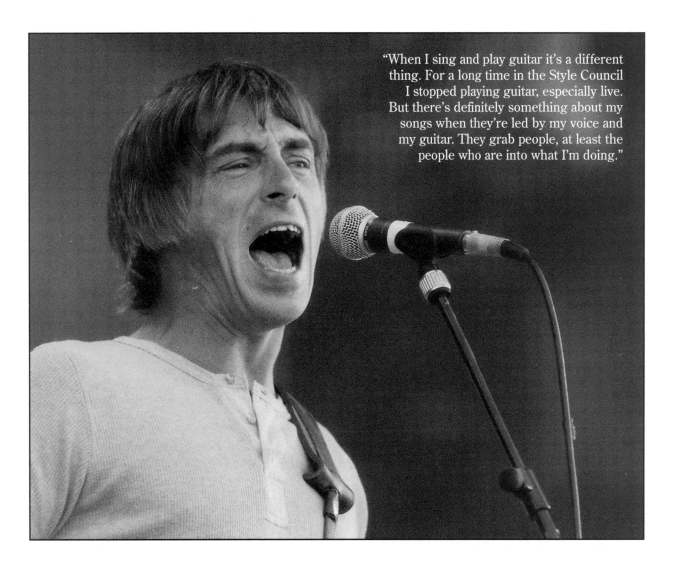

"When I sing and play guitar it's a different thing. For a long time in the Style Council I stopped playing guitar, especially live. But there's definitely something about my songs when they're led by my voice and my guitar. They grab people, at least the people who are into what I'm doing."

Riff 7a

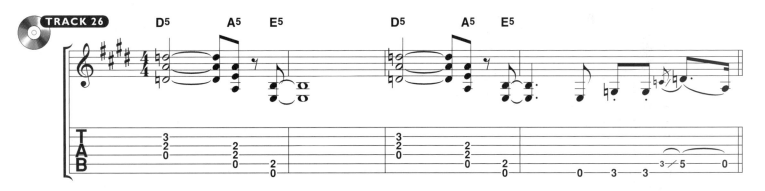

Riff 7b

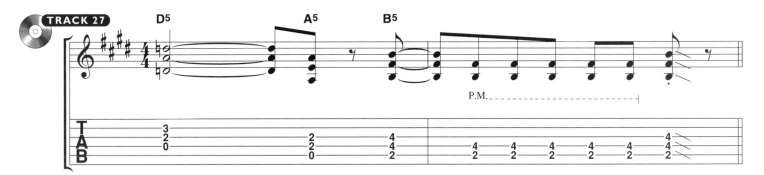

These two riffs are combined to complete the bridge section. They are simple power chord riffs differing only in the last bar.

This section contrasts with the laid back feel of the earlier parts so go for a more pushy feel and a more distorted sound.

Rhythm Riff 1

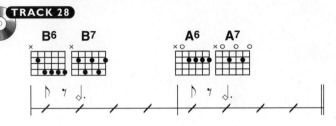

These are two bar riffs that are played together in each verse. In Rhythm Riff 1 keep the first chord in each bar (B6 and A6) short and sharp. In Rhythm Riff 2 play the B5 and A5 with palm muting.

Rhythm Riff 2

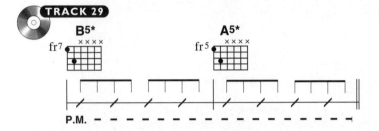

Rhythm Riff 3

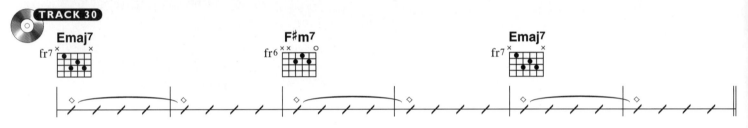

This Rhythm Riff is used to accompany the guitar solo – play the chords as soft slow arpeggios.

Rhythm Riff 4a

These Riffs are used in the outro in combination with Riff 1. (Rhythm Riff 4c is heard in the background behind Riff 1c.) All three are based on Riff 2 so use the same shapes and play the Gmaj7 and A chords accented and short. Use the same warm distorted sound as for Riff 2.

Rhythm Riff 4b

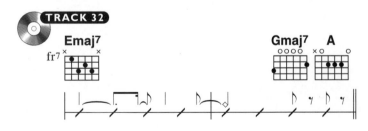

Rhythm Riff 4c

RIFF BY RIFF: PAUL WELLER

RIFF ROUTE MAPS

ALL THE PICTURES ON THE WALL
Riff Route Map

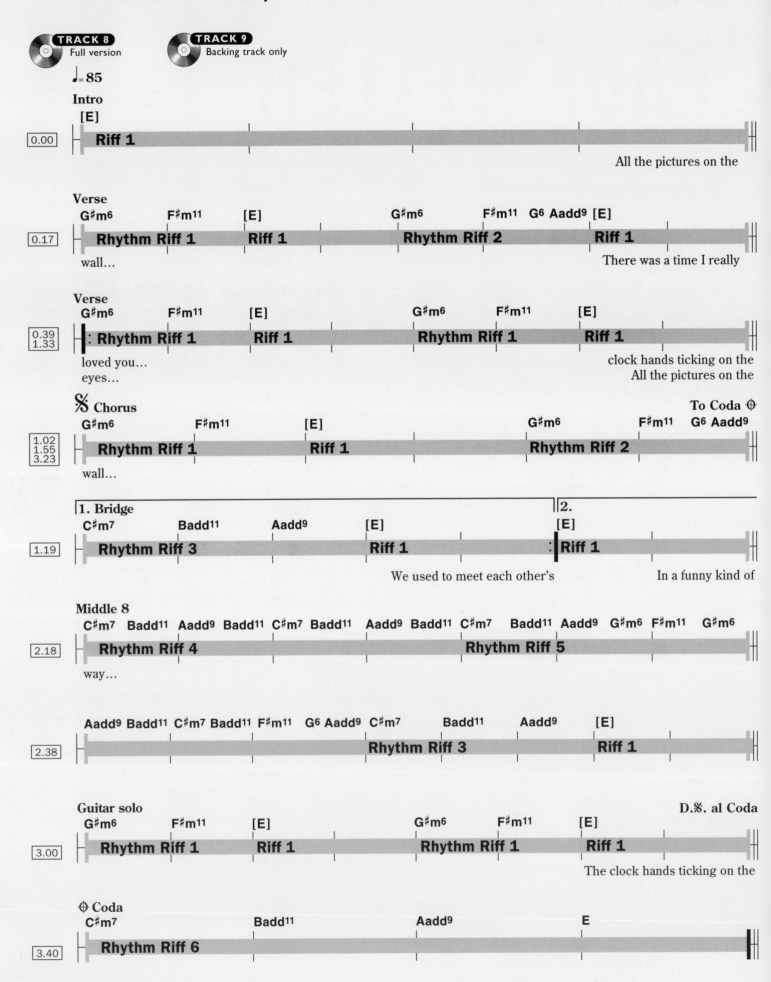

Riff by Riff...Paul Weller *Page 2*

INTO TOMORROW
Riff Route Map

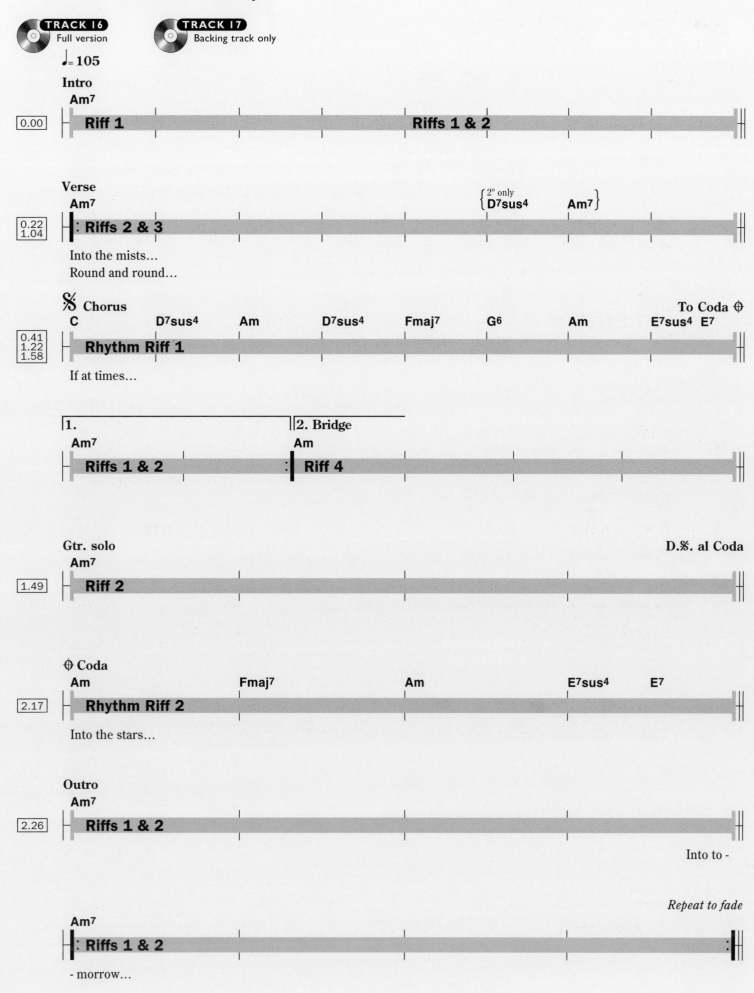

OUT OF THE SINKING
Riff Route Map

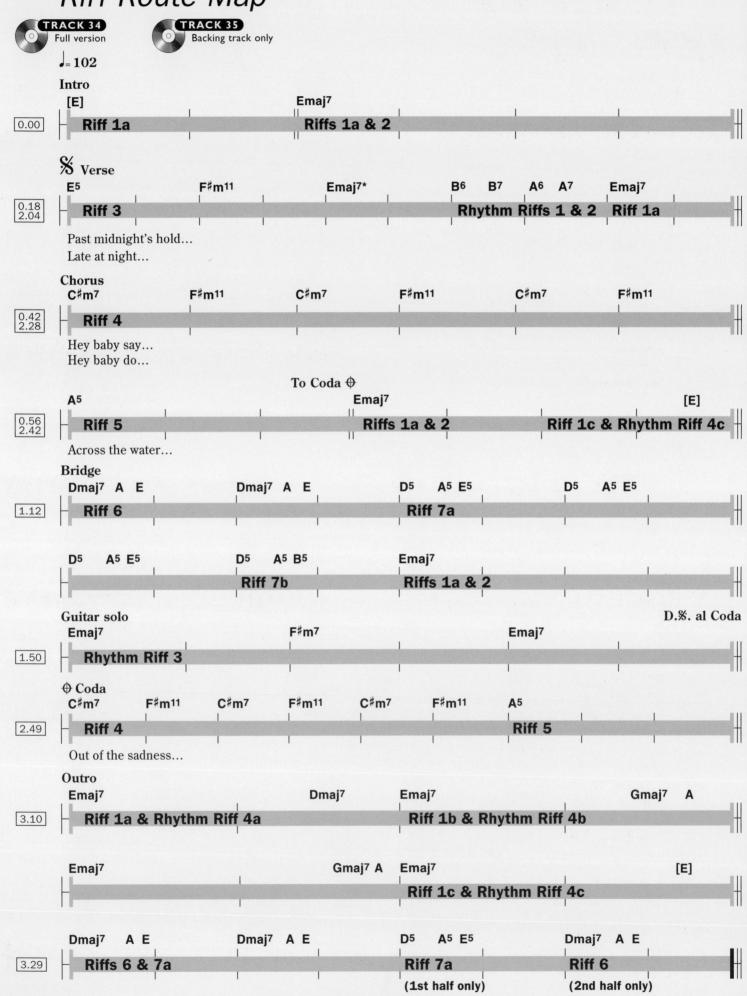

PEACOCK SUIT
Riff Route Map

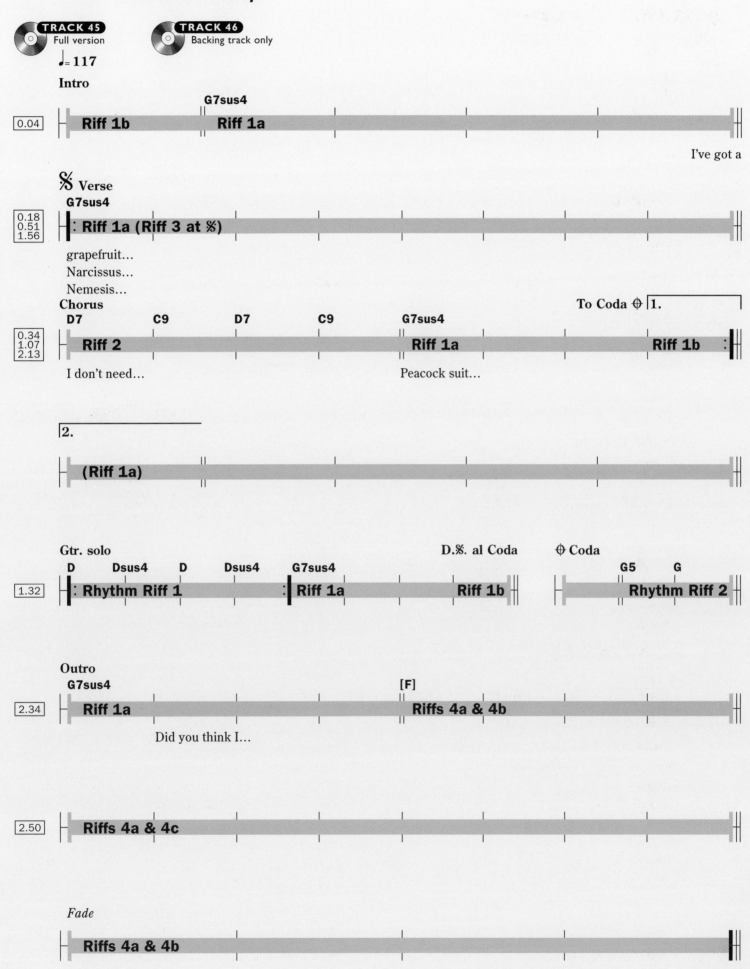

SUNFLOWER
Riff Route Map

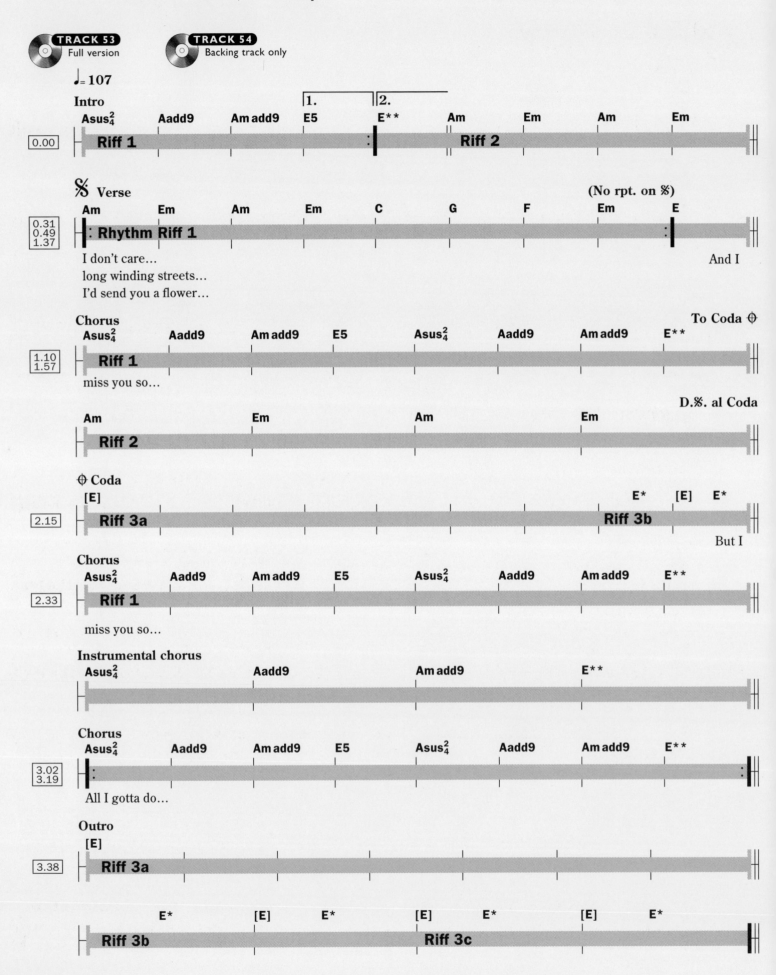

THE CHANGINGMAN
Riff Route Map

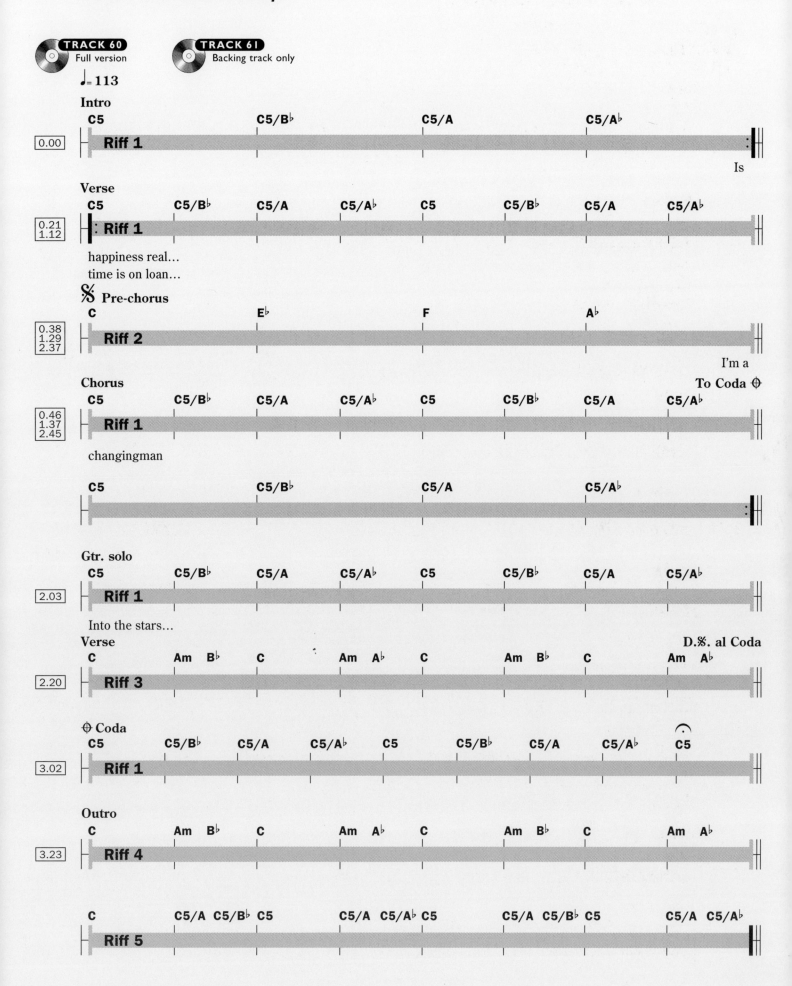

WOODCUTTER'S SON
Riff Route Map

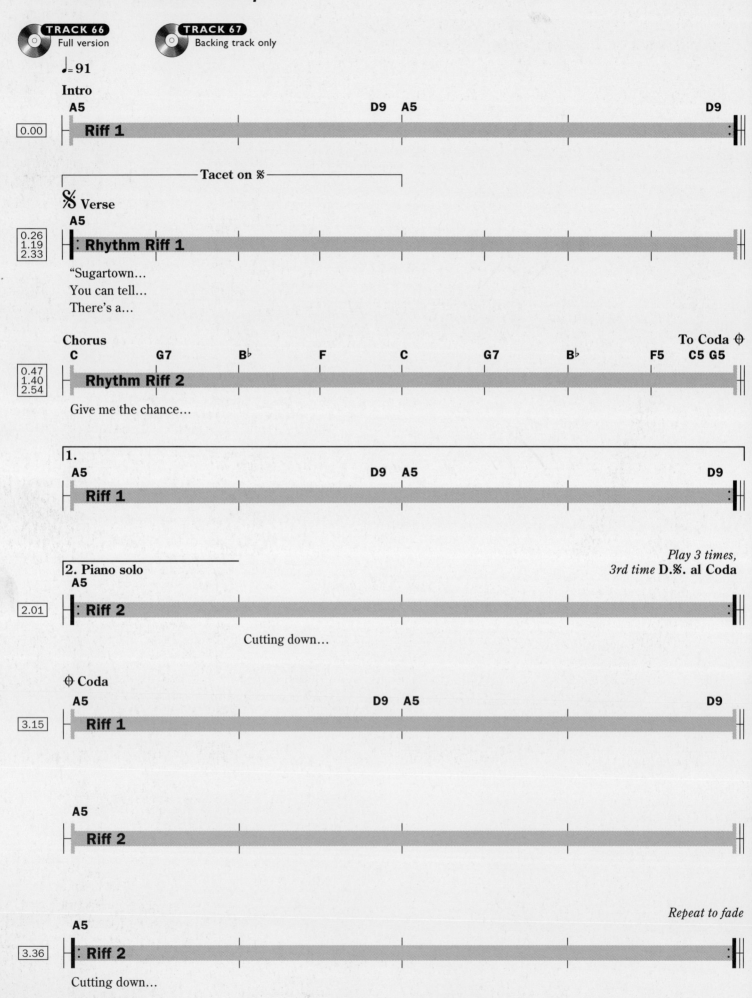

"I suppose in some ways I write in an old-fashioned way because I always have middle-eights in my songs and not many people do any more. It's usually just a verse and chorus. Structure is really important. Some I've really had to work at, others come really quickly. Keeping the whole thing interesting, that's what it all comes down to."

OUT OF THE SINKING
Riff Route Map

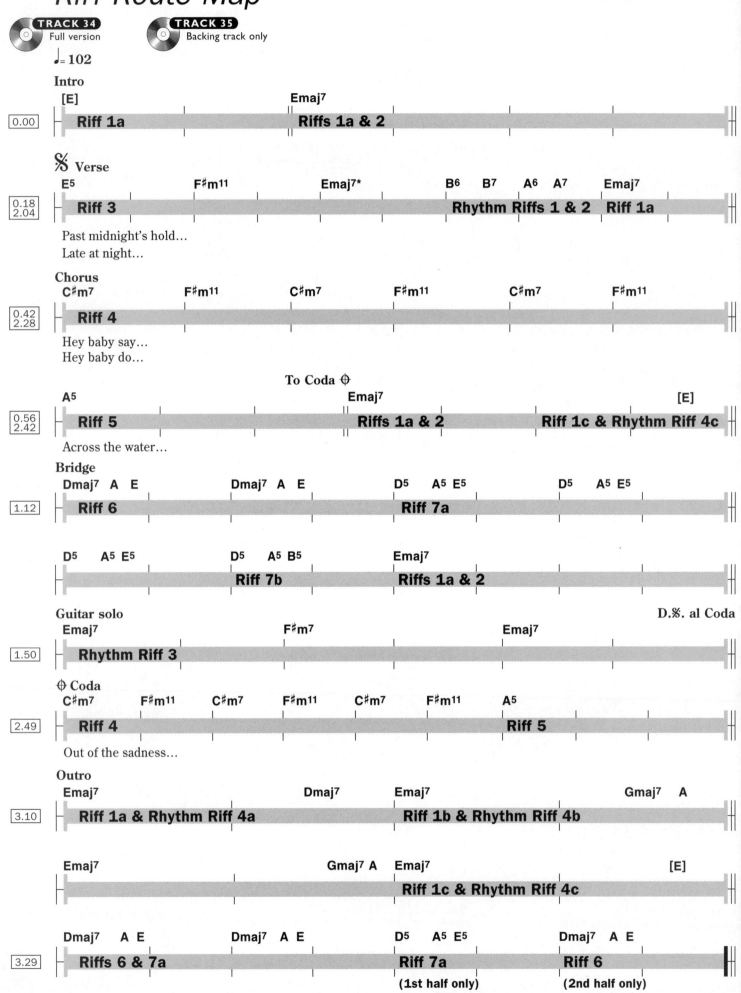

OUT OF THE SINKING
Lyrics

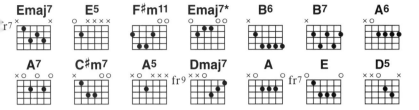

Intro: Emaj7 (6 bars)

Verse 1:
E5
Past midnight's hold
F♯m11
Where the world's awaiting
Emaj7*
I'll wait for your love
B6 B7   A6 A7
But I close my eyes, as there's pain
                Emaj7
  too in paradise
And we pay the price.

Chorus 1:
C♯m7   F♯m11
Hey baby say just what you're thinking
C♯m7   F♯m11
Know I feel it – Yeh feel I'm sinking
C♯m7   F♯m11
Know I know it – I know you feel it too
A5
Across the water, there's a boat
                Emaj7
  that will take us away.

Bridge: (4 bars)   Dmaj7 A E
                        Dmaj7 A E

D5   A5   E5
It is shining for me
D5   A5   E5
All I need to be
D5   A5   E5
But I can't find the key
D5   A5   E5
The one to make me believe.

Guitar: (4 bars)   Emaj7
            (6 bars)   Emaj7 F♯m7 Emaj7

Verse 2:
E5
Late at night
F♯m11
When the world is dreaming
Emaj7*
Way past the stars
B6 B7   A6 A7
That ignore our fate and twinkle
                Emaj7
  too late to save us
So we save ourselves.

Chorus 2:
C♯m7   F♯m11
Hey baby say just what you're thinking
C♯m7   F♯m11
Know I know it – Yeh feel I'm sinking
C♯m7   F♯m11
Know I feel it – I know you feel it too
A5
Across the water, there's a boat that
  will take us away.

Coda:
C♯m7   F♯m11
Far from the madness – out of the
  sadness
C♯m7   F♯m11
Into the sunlight – out of the sinking
C♯m7   F♯m11
You know I feel it
C♯m7   F♯m11
I know you feel it too
A5
Across the water, there's a boat that
  will take us away.
Emaj7
And there we'll stay.

Outro: (16 bars)

PEACOCK SUIT

Words and Music by Paul Weller

'Peacock Suit' was released as a single in August 1996 and also featured on Weller's 1997 album *Heavy Soul*. Never afraid to experiment, he manages to combine influences from rock of the early seventies with glimpses of a previous era, but still manages to stamp his own unmistakable style on the song.

The song opens with a 'strut rock' figure, helped by a dirty guitar sound; the chorus then lapses into an off-beat chordal riff, reminiscent of the Beatles – all firmly based in a bluesy mould. The whole effect is driven by a gutsy, throbbing bass and Paul's no-non-sense vocal style.

Riff 1a

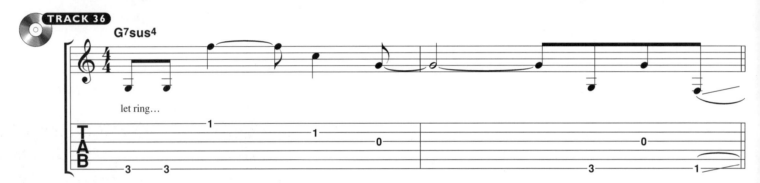

This is a trademark Paul Weller riff and is used in both the verses and chorus. The riff is based around the G7sus4 chord (see chord box on page 29) so use this shape, keeping your third finger on the bottom string to slide between F and G. Paul often varies this riff, so don't be afraid to experiment. Use the bridge pickup with plenty of distortion to get that twangy sound.

Riff 1b

This riff is used in the opening of the song and is a pickup into each verse. Keep the slurs rhythmic and clean and follow the picking direction as marked – this will help you to skip the open D string cleanly. Try picking close to the bridge for extra attack.

Riff 2

TRACK 38

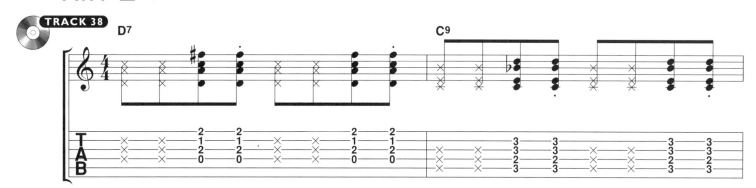

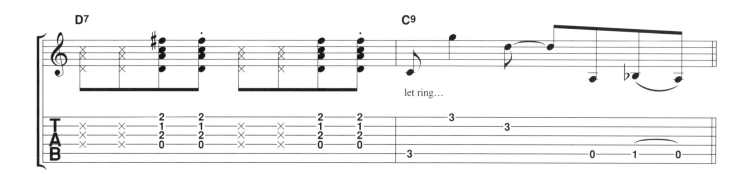

This choppy chord riff is heard in the chorus. Use your fretting hand to deaden the strings for the muted chords and keep the last chord in each bar short and sharp. The last bar of the riff is a pickup into Riff 1. Go for a rigid rhythmic feel – this will contrast well with the looseness of the rest of the song.

Riff 3

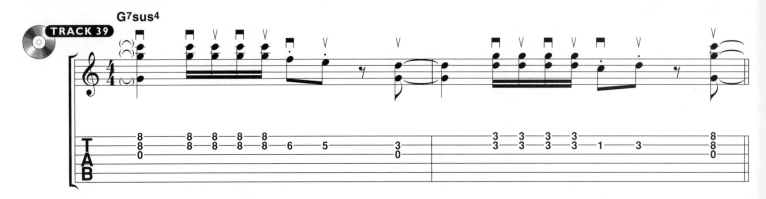

This riff is used in the third verse (in addition to Riff 1). This should be played with a loose feel. If you follow the picking direction as marked you'll find the riff easier to play, and the feel will be closer to the original. Again, you can vary this one.

Riff 4a

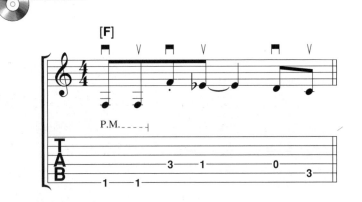

These are all versions of the same basic riff and are used in different combinations in the outro of the song. Riff 4a plays right through (in the right channel) while the other guitar plays either Riff 4b or Riff 4c (in the left channel). Use palm muting on the first two notes, keeping them very short; the third note is not muted but is also kept short. Accentuate the difference between the muted and open notes.

Riff 4b

Riff 4c

Rhythm Riff 1

TRACK 43

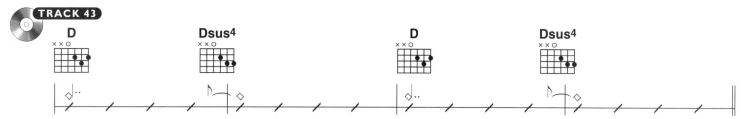

These chords are used behind the guitar solo. The D chord is played on the beat while the Dsus4 chords are syncopated (played slightly before the downbeat of the next bar).

Rhythm Riff 2

TRACK 44

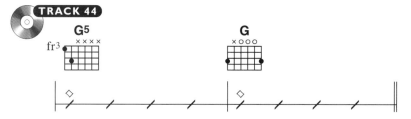

These two bars give the song some breathing space before the extended outro begins.

"My songwriting's become more personalised, but I wouldn't really call it introverted. I'm writing maybe more from... I was gonna say from a personal angle, but I think I always have done anyway. Maybe it shows more now."

PEACOCK SUIT
Riff Route Map

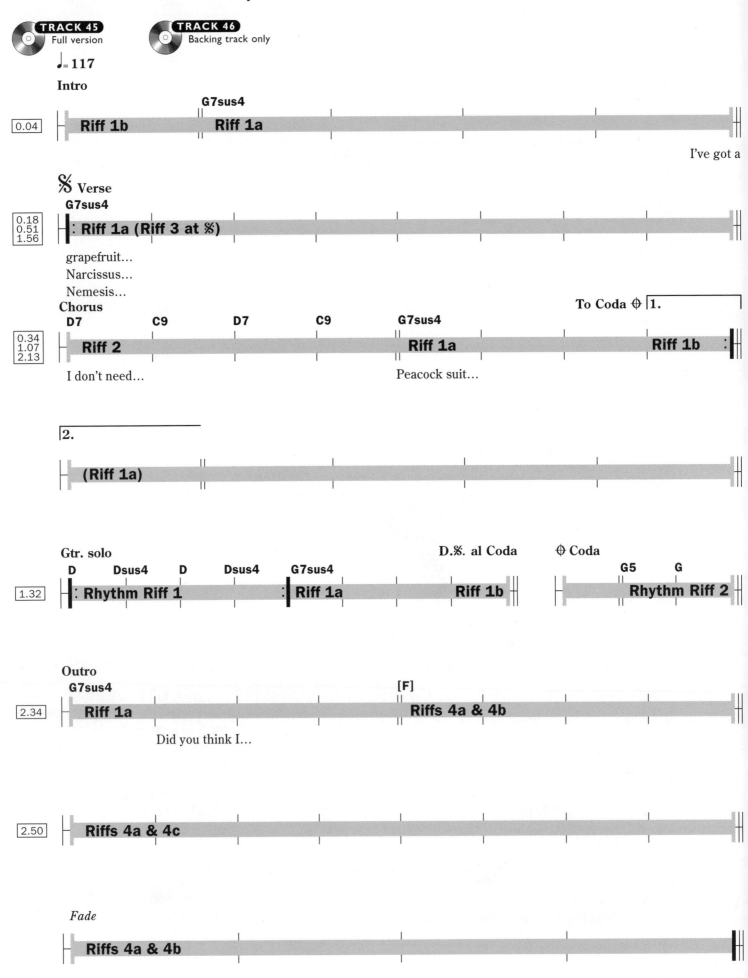

PEACOCK SUIT
Lyrics

G7sus4 **D7** **C9**

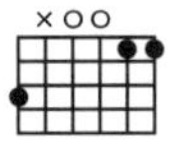

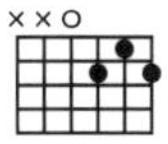

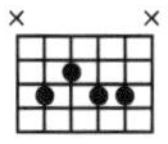

Intro: **G7sus4**
(5 bars)

Verse 1: **G7sus4**
I've got a grapefruit matter,
It's as sour as shit.
I have no solutions,
Better get used to it.

Chorus 1: **D7** **C9**
I don't need a ship to sail in stormy
  weather.
D7 **C9**
I don't need you to ruffle the feathers
  G7sus4
  of my peacock suit.

Verse 2: **G7sus4**
I'm Narcissus in a puddle,
In shop windows I gloat.
Like a ball of fleece lining,
In my camel skin coat.

Chorus 2: (As Chorus 1)

Gtr solo: (12 bars)

Verse 3: **G7sus4**
Nemesis in a muddle,
In a mirror I look.
Like a streak of sheet lightning!
In my rattlesnake shoes.

Chorus 3: (As Chorus 1)

Outro: Did you fink I should!

Fade: (4 bars)

"Hopefully, being moved by music is a process that will always happen. The day you don't get inspired by something is when you know it's over."

SUNFLOWER

Words and Music by Paul Weller
© Copyright 1993 Notting Hill Music (UK) Limited,
8B Berkeley Gardens, London W8 4AP.
All Rights Reserved. International Copyright Secured.

'Sunflower' is the first track on the 1993 album *Wild Wood*. It begins with an arpeggio riff on guitar which, with the help of a mellotron flute line, immediately evokes the Psychedelic era. The pick-up into the verse and the verse itself are supported by some heavier, rockier rhythm riffs - these should be played with conviction. Once you have learned the examples below don't be afraid to experiment with these riffs – this style of playing can be a useful addition to a guitarist's repertoire.

Riff 1

TRACK 47

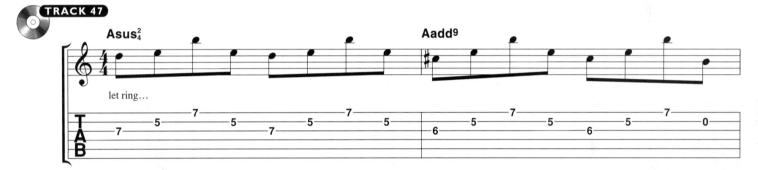

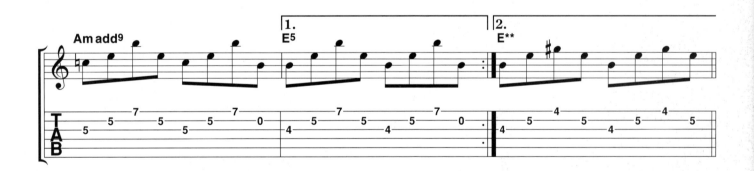

This is a ringing arpeggio riff that opens the song and is the basis of the chorus. The top two notes stay the same whilst the bottom note moves down chromatically. This may cause some fingering difficulty – however, the open string at the end of bar 2 will give you a chance to change fingers.

In bar 3 use your first finger to barre the second and third string, again using the open string at the end to help smooth out the fingering change. Use the bridge pickup with a slightly distorted sound.

Riff 2

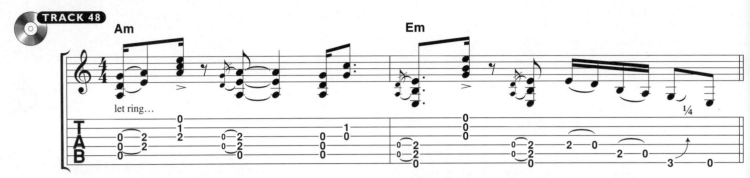

This riff is used in the second half of the intro and as a pickup into the second verse. There are a lot of hammer-ons and pull-offs here, so try to keep them rhythmic – don't rush them. Notice the accents on the off-beat chords.

Riff 3a

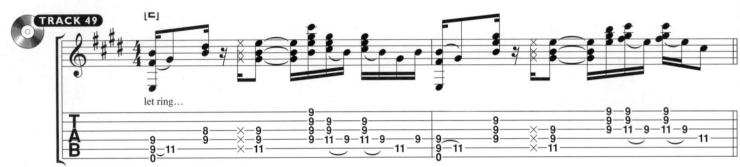

Riff 3b

Riff 3c

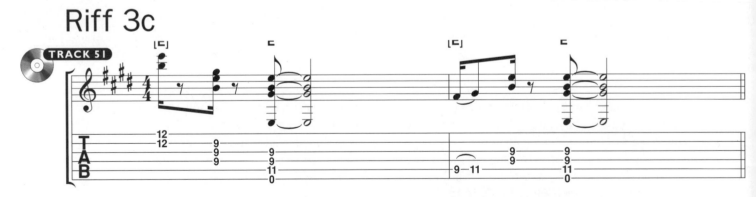

These variations of the same riff occur throughout the coda section and right at the end of the song. Although they may look complex they're actually easy. All the notes are in the same position, the only tricky part is keeping the chords ringing above the moving notes – make sure your fingers are well arched so you don't accidently damp the strings. Aim for a funky, syncopated feel.

"Play in front of anybody, your friends, your mum and dad, anything to get it out of the bedroom and gain a little self-confidence. Play along to records... forget all the rules, do whatever you think, do whatever sounds good to you."

Rhythm Riff 1

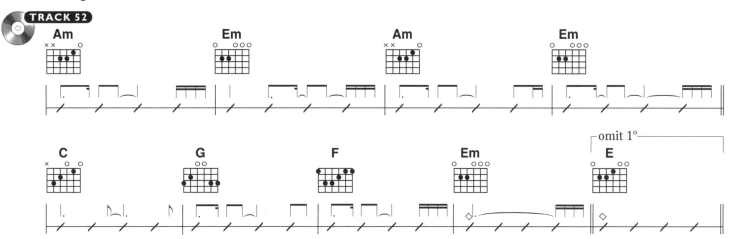

TRACK 52

This is the chord progression used in the verse. If you listen carefully to the recording you'll hear that Paul doesn't always play the full chord on each strike.

This is to give more "space" to the vocal, and to bring the energy level down for the verse so that it can be increased for the chorus.

SUNFLOWER
Riff Route Map

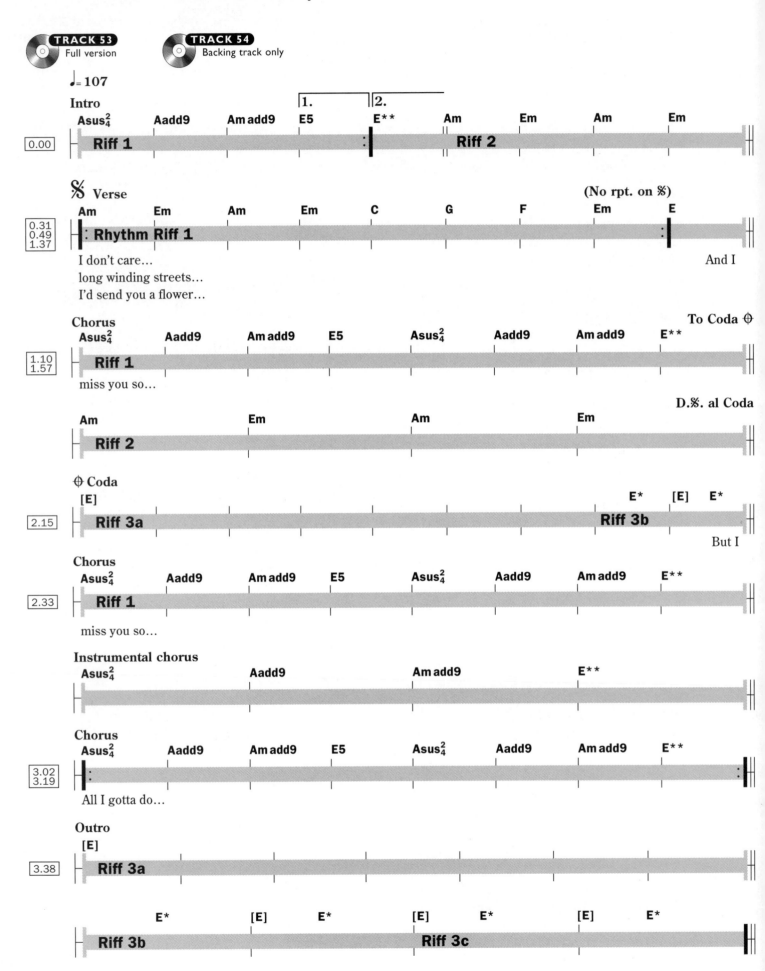

SUNFLOWER
Lyrics

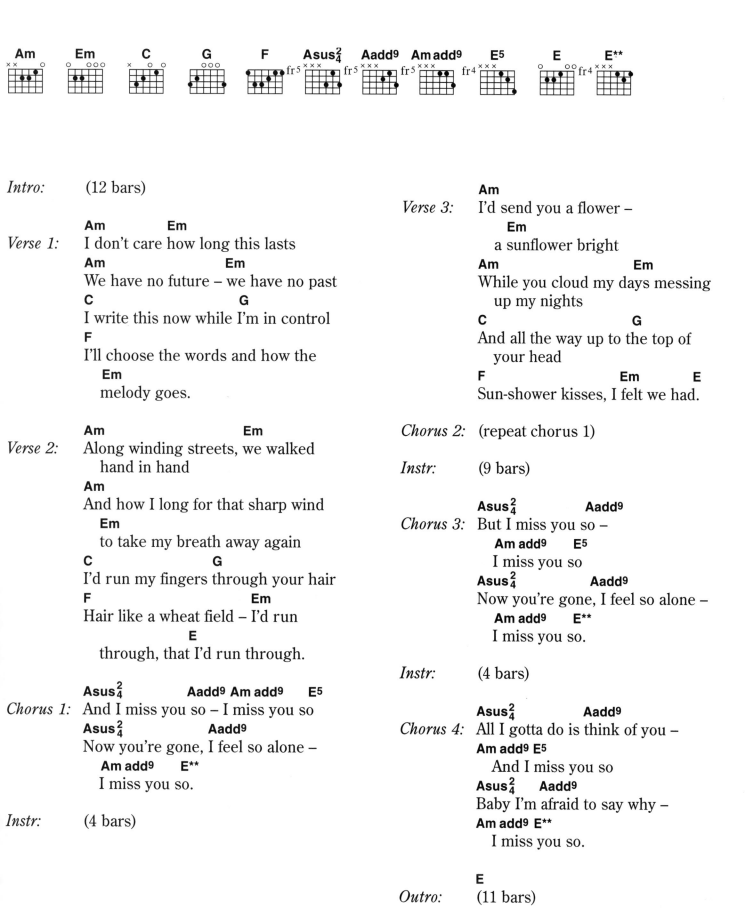

Am   Em   C   G   F   Asus$^2_4$ Aadd⁹   Am add⁹   E⁵   E   E**

Intro: (12 bars)

Verse 1:
   Am   **Em**
I don't care how long this lasts
   Am   **Em**
We have no future – we have no past
C   **G**
I write this now while I'm in control
F
I'll choose the words and how the
   Em
    melody goes.

Verse 2:
   Am   **Em**
Along winding streets, we walked
    hand in hand
   Am
And how I long for that sharp wind
   Em
    to take my breath away again
C   **G**
I'd run my fingers through your hair
F   **Em**
Hair like a wheat field – I'd run
         E
    through, that I'd run through.

Chorus 1:
   Asus$^2_4$ **Aadd⁹ Am add⁹**   **E⁵**
And I miss you so – I miss you so
   Asus$^2_4$ **Aadd⁹**
Now you're gone, I feel so alone –
   Am add⁹   **E****
    I miss you so.

Instr: (4 bars)

Verse 3:
   Am
I'd send you a flower –
   Em
    a sunflower bright
Am   **Em**
While you cloud my days messing
    up my nights
C   **G**
And all the way up to the top of
    your head
F   **Em**   **E**
Sun-shower kisses, I felt we had.

Chorus 2:   (repeat chorus 1)

Instr: (9 bars)

Chorus 3:
   Asus$^2_4$ **Aadd⁹**
But I miss you so –
   Am add⁹   **E⁵**
    I miss you so
   Asus$^2_4$ **Aadd⁹**
Now you're gone, I feel so alone –
   Am add⁹   **E****
    I miss you so.

Instr: (4 bars)

Chorus 4:
   Asus$^2_4$ **Aadd⁹**
All I gotta do is think of you –
   Am add⁹ E⁵
    And I miss you so
   Asus$^2_4$ **Aadd⁹**
Baby I'm afraid to say why –
   Am add⁹ E**
    I miss you so.

Outro:
   E
(11 bars)

THE CHANGINGMAN

Words and Music by Paul Weller & Brendan Lynch
© Copyright 1995 Stylist Music Limited/
BMG Music Publishing Limited, 69-79 Fulham High Street, London SW6 (80%)
& Notting Hill Music (UK) Limited, 8B Berkeley Gardens, London W8 (20%).
This arrangement © Copyright 1997 BMG Music Publishing Limited for their share.
All Rights Reserved. International Copyright Secured.

A top ten hit in 1995, 'The Changingman' is the opening track on the album *Stanley Road*. It's a powerful rock song with a hint of psychedelic influence. This is most apparent in the main riff, an arpeggio passage with a descending bass line – this is well worth practising as it can be utilised to form the basis of many guitar accompaniments.

Riff 1

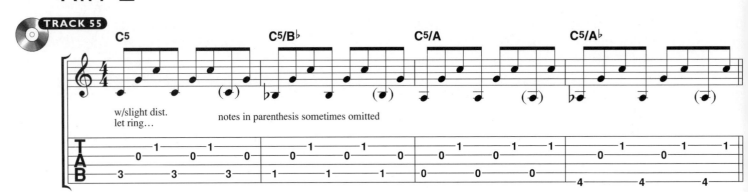

This opening arpeggio riff uses a musical idea that is common in Paul Weller's music – a descending bass line with static top notes. It's used for most of the song – verse, chorus and outro (in various forms). It's important to keep the strings ringing on this riff which may be tricky unless you use the correct fingering. Start by holding down an open C chord – this is the basis of the riff. You only need to use your first and fourth fingers for the first bar – when the bass note drops, play it with your second finger, then release to the open A with a final stretch with your fifth finger to the A♭. Although some of these shapes might seem awkward at first, with a little practice you'll soon get the hang of it. Use a slightly distorted sound with the bridge pickup.

Riff 2

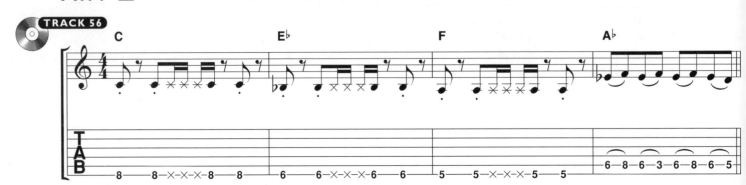

This percussive single-note riff, used in the pre-chorus, is a good deal easier than Riff 1. Technically, it shouldn't pose too many problems, but try to capture the feel of the original. The notes marked with a staccato dot should be short and sharp, contrasting with the slurred notes in the last bar. The muted notes are very important to the rhythm of the riffs, so try to keep the rhythm steady as you play them. The sound should be slightly more distorted than Riff 1 to give the part more body.

Riff 3

TRACK 57

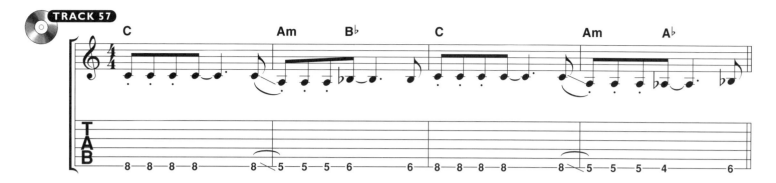

This is another percussive single note riff, this time used as an alternative part for the second verse.

Keep all the notes short (except for the slide-down in the first and third bars) and concentrate on getting a good feel for the rhythm.

Riff 4

TRACK 58

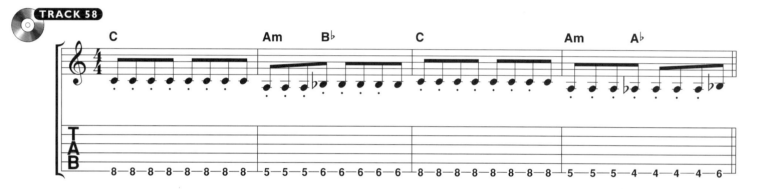

Riff 4 fills out Riff 3 with a steady, robotic rhythm. Once again, capturing the feel of the original is the key to making this sound good.

Riff 5

TRACK 59

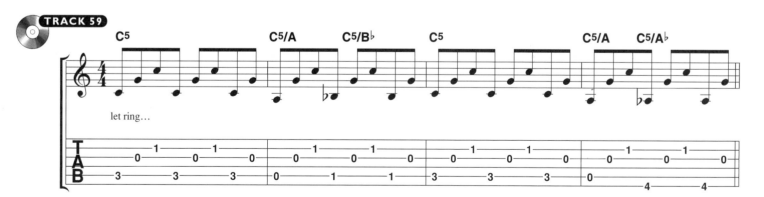

This riff is used in the outro and is a combination of Riff 1 and Riff 3. It has the bass notes from Riff 3 and the arpeggio pattern from Riff 1.

Keep the same approach to fingering as in Riff 1 – watch out for those tricky shapes and try to keep the strings ringing.

THE CHANGINGMAN
Riff Route Map

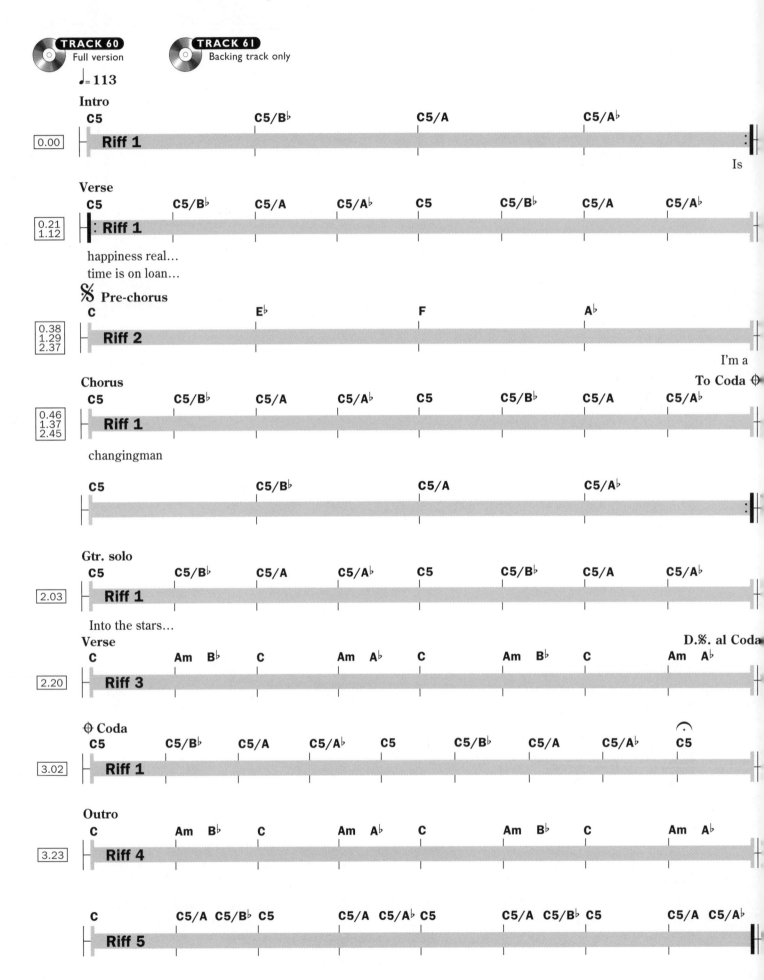

THE CHANGINGMAN
Lyrics

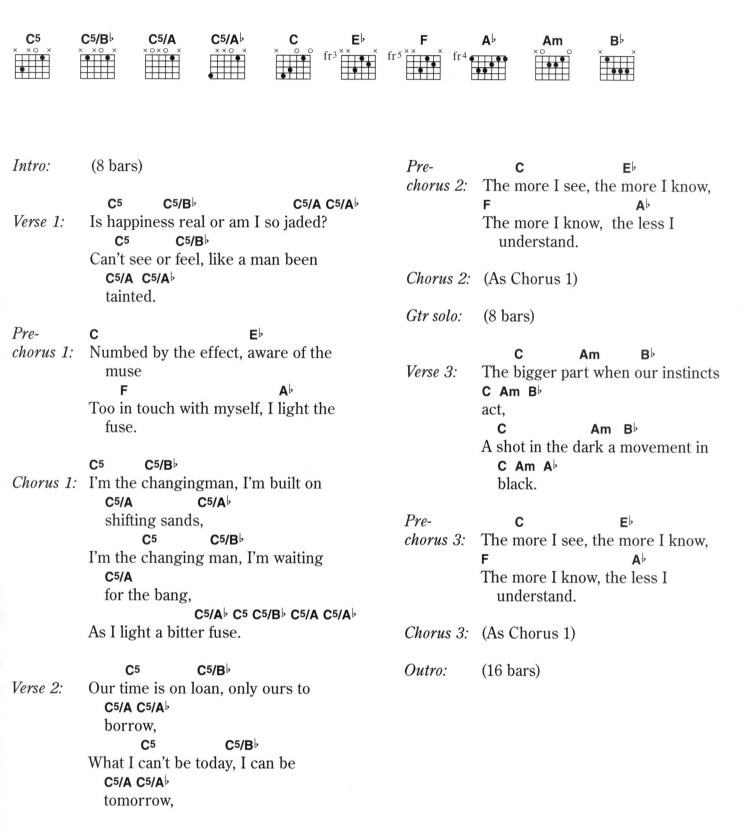

C5 C5/B♭ C5/A C5/A♭ C E♭ F A♭ Am B♭

Intro: (8 bars)

Verse 1:
      C5   C5/B♭   C5/A C5/A♭
Is happiness real or am I so jaded?
      C5   C5/B♭
Can't see or feel, like a man been
      C5/A C5/A♭
tainted.

Pre-chorus 1:
    C   E♭
Numbed by the effect, aware of the
    muse
    F   A♭
Too in touch with myself, I light the
    fuse.

Chorus 1:
    C5   C5/B♭
I'm the changingman, I'm built on
    C5/A   C5/A♭
shifting sands,
      C5   C5/B♭
I'm the changing man, I'm waiting
    C5/A
for the bang,
        C5/A♭ C5 C5/B♭ C5/A C5/A♭
As I light a bitter fuse.

Verse 2:
    C5   C5/B♭
Our time is on loan, only ours to
    C5/A C5/A♭
borrow,
      C5   C5/B♭
What I can't be today, I can be
    C5/A C5/A♭
tomorrow,

Pre-chorus 2:
    C   E♭
The more I see, the more I know,
    F   A♭
The more I know, the less I
    understand.

Chorus 2: (As Chorus 1)

Gtr solo: (8 bars)

Verse 3:
    C   Am   B♭
The bigger part when our instincts
C Am B♭
act,
    C   Am   B♭
A shot in the dark a movement in
C Am A♭
black.

Pre-chorus 3:
    C   E♭
The more I see, the more I know,
    F   A♭
The more I know, the less I
    understand.

Chorus 3: (As Chorus 1)

Outro: (16 bars)

WOODCUTTER'S SON

Words and Music by Paul Weller
© Copyright 1995 Stylist Music Limited/
BMG Music Publishing Limited, 69/79 Fulham High Street, London SW6.
This arrangement © 1997 BMG Music Publishing Limited.
All Rights Reserved. International Copyright Secured.

This is the 5th track on the hugely successful album *Stanley Road*. It's a raunchy rhythm and blues composition, with ex-Traffic star Stevie Winwood adding a touch of authenticity on keyboards.

Although the guitar leaves plenty of space in this number for keyboards and vocals, it does play an important role in introducing new sections and supporting the freer elements of the song. Distortion is used to give that extra raunchiness to the guitar sound.

Riff 1

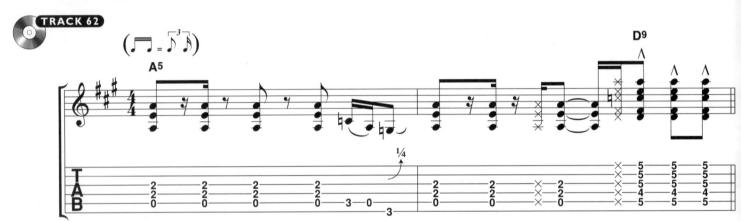

This is a simple riff that has to be played with conviction. Concentrate on perfecting the pull-offs and decorative bends. The rhythm has a swing feel – all of the off-beats are played slightly late. This can take some getting used to especially when playing muted chords as in the second bar – listen carefully to the recording. The D9 chords at the end of the second bar should be stacatto and accented (short and loud). Use the bridge pick-up with a full distorted sound.

Riff 2

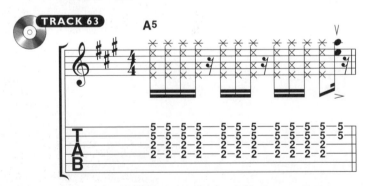

This rhythmic riff is used in the middle breakdown of the song and also at the end. For the muted parts keep the chord shape without holding down the strings. Use a sharp upstroke for the chord at the end of the bar. Try for the same swinging feel as Riff 1.

Rhythm Riff 1

TRACK 64

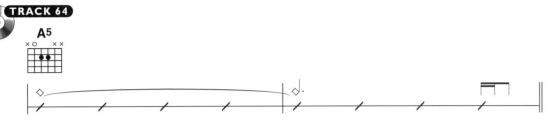

The A5 chord is played over the verse using this rhythm. Each of the verses is slightly different so feel free to experiment.

Notice how Paul isn't afraid to leave gaps in his playing – giving the music a chance to breathe.

Rhythm Riff 2

TRACK 65

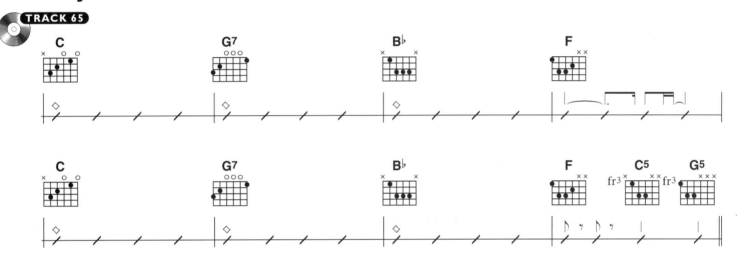

This is the chord progression of the chorus. Most of the chords are hit once at the start of the bar, except for the F chord which plays along with a piano fill.

WOODCUTTER'S SON
Riff Route Map

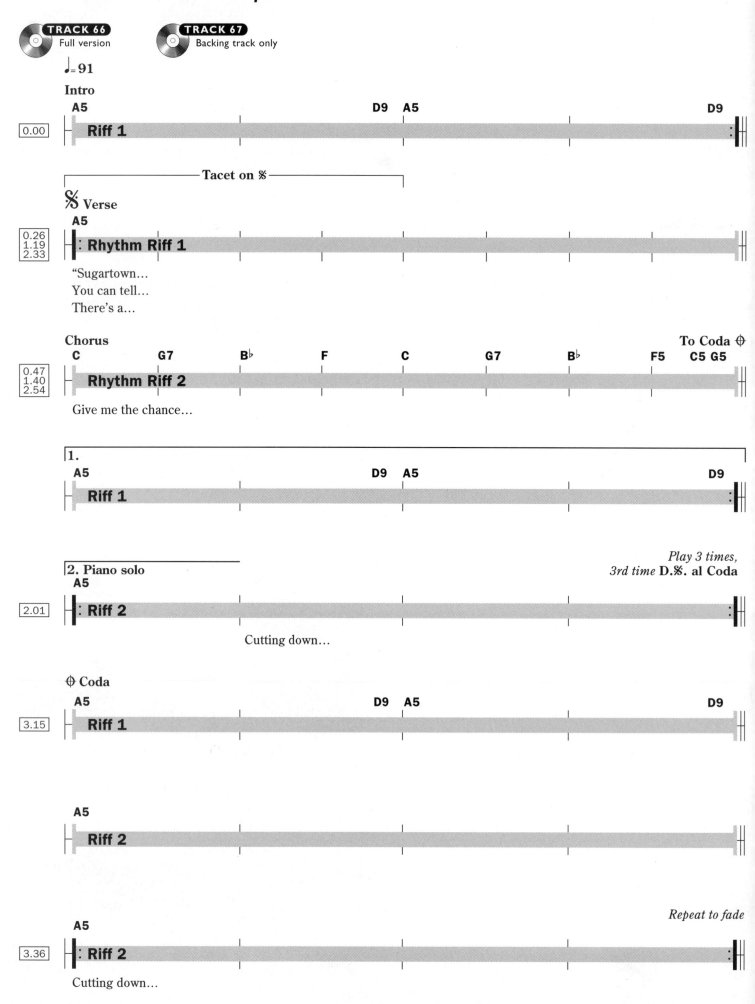

WOODCUTTER'S SON
Lyrics

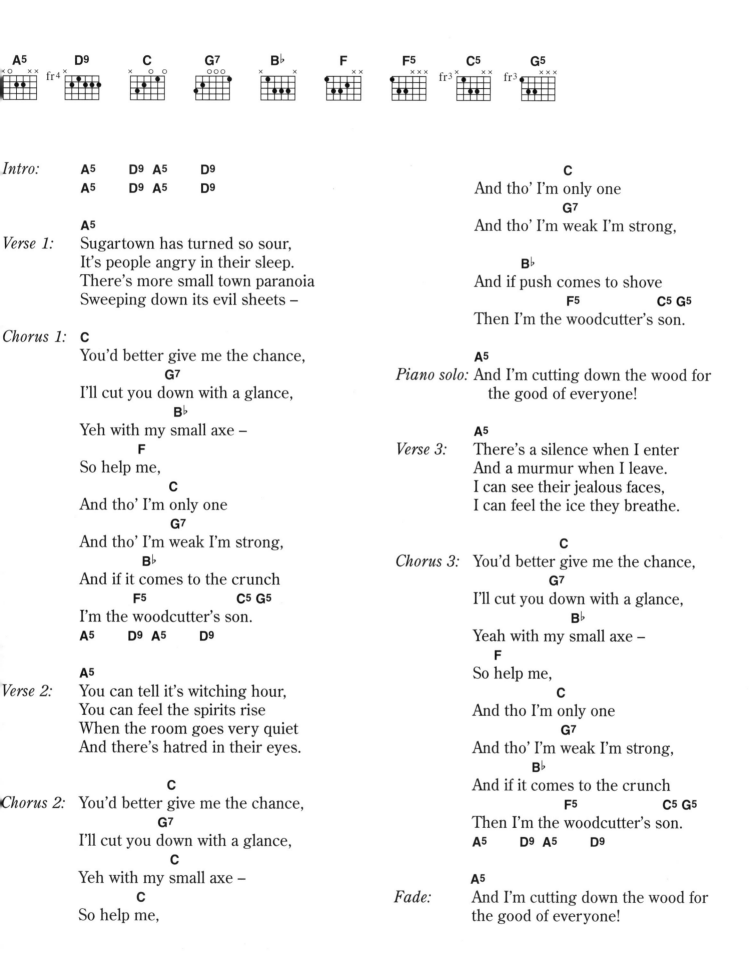

A5   **D9**   **C**   **G7**   **B♭**   **F**   **F5**   **C5**   **G5**

Intro: **A5**   **D9** **A5**   **D9**
          A5   **D9** **A5**   **D9**

          A5
Verse 1:   Sugartown has turned so sour,
           It's people angry in their sleep.
           There's more small town paranoia
           Sweeping down its evil sheets –

Chorus 1:   **C**
           You'd better give me the chance,
             G7
           I'll cut you down with a glance,
             B♭
           Yeh with my small axe –
             F
           So help me,
             C
           And tho' I'm only one
             G7
           And tho' I'm weak I'm strong,
             B♭
           And if it comes to the crunch
             F5   **C5 G5**
           I'm the woodcutter's son.
           A5   **D9** **A5**   **D9**

          A5
Verse 2:   You can tell it's witching hour,
           You can feel the spirits rise
           When the room goes very quiet
           And there's hatred in their eyes.

             C
Chorus 2:   You'd better give me the chance,
             G7
           I'll cut you down with a glance,
             C
           Yeh with my small axe –
             C
           So help me,

             C
           And tho' I'm only one
             G7
           And tho' I'm weak I'm strong,

             B♭
           And if push comes to shove
             F5   **C5 G5**
           Then I'm the woodcutter's son.

             A5
Piano solo: And I'm cutting down the wood for
             the good of everyone!

             A5
Verse 3:   There's a silence when I enter
           And a murmur when I leave.
           I can see their jealous faces,
           I can feel the ice they breathe.

             C
Chorus 3:   You'd better give me the chance,
             G7
           I'll cut you down with a glance,
             B♭
           Yeah with my small axe –
             F
           So help me,
             C
           And tho I'm only one
             G7
           And tho' I'm weak I'm strong,
             B♭
           And if it comes to the crunch
             F5   **C5 G5**
           Then I'm the woodcutter's son.
           A5   **D9** **A5**   **D9**

             A5
Fade: And I'm cutting down the wood for
           the good of everyone!

FURTHER READING

If you've enjoyed exploring Paul Weller's music in this book, why not check out some of the other exciting titles available:

The Jam - Greatest Hits
(Guitar Tab/Vocal)
Order No. AM950246
11 of The Jam's best songs in standard and guitar tablature notation with vocals. Includes 'Start', 'The Eton Rifles', 'That's Entertainment', 'Town Called Malice', 'Going Underground', 'The Bitterest Pill (I Ever Had To Swallow)', 'Precious', 'Strange Town', 'Absolute Beginners' & 'Funeral Pyre'.

Paul Weller - The Best Of
(Piano/Vocal/Guitar)
Order No. AM931953
A selection of his best songs arranged for piano, voice and guitar, with lyrics and chords. Includes 'Into Tomorrow', 'Wild Wood', 'Sunflower', '5th Season', 'Above The Clouds' and 'Bull-Rush'.

Paul Weller - The Chord Songbook
(Guitar Chords/Lyrics)
Order No. AM942546
20 of Paul's most popular songs from his solo career in one concise collection, featuring complete lyrics and guitar chord boxes. Songs include 'The Weaver', 'You Do Something To Me', 'Wild Wood', 'Sunflower', 'Remember How We Started', 'Stanley Road', 'The Changingman', 'Shadow Of The Sun', '5th Season', 'Has My Fire Really Gone Out?' and 'Bitterness Rising'.

Paul Weller - For Easy Guitar
(Easy Guitar Tab/Vocal)
Order No. AM951346
Thirteen hit songs simplified for guitar in easy-to-read tablature and standard notation, complete with guitar chord boxes and lyrics. Taken from all four of his solo albums, songs include 'Friday Street', 'The Changingman', 'Out Of The Sinking', 'Into Tomorrow', 'Mermaids', 'Bull-Rush' & 'The Weaver'.

Paul Weller - For Guitar Tab
(Guitar Tab/Vocal)
Order No. AM935847
Eleven great songs in guitar tablature and standard notation with melody line, lyrics and chords. Songs include 'Into Tomorrow', 'The Changingman', 'Out Of The Sinking', 'Sunflower' and 'Has My Fire Really Gone Out?'.

Paul Weller - Heavy Soul
(Guitar Tab/Vocal)
Order No. AM950477
Matching folio to Paul's latest album, authentically transcribed in both standard and guitar tablature notation, plus lyrics and chords. Includes 'Peacock Suit', 'Friday Street', 'Brushed', 'Up In Suze's Room', 'Mermaids' and 'I Should Have Been There To Inspire You'.

Paul Weller - Paul Weller
(Piano/Vocal/Guitar)
Order No. AM90230
All the songs from his 1992 debut solo album arranged for piano, voice and guitar. Includes the hit singles 'Into Tomorrow', 'Uh Huh Oh Yeh' and 'Above The Clouds'.

Paul Weller - Play Guitar With: Book & CD
(Guitar Tab/Vocal)
Order No. AM937827
Step into Paul's shoes to play 8 of his best songs along with the live recorded backing tracks that sound just like the recordings! The book contains transcriptions in tablature, lyrics and chords. Includes 'Wild Wood', 'Out Of The Sinking', 'Into Tomorrow', 'Stanley Road', 'The Changingman', 'Sunflower' and 'Woodcutter's Son'.

Paul Weller - Stanley Road
(Guitar Tab/Vocal)
Order No. AM944614
Every song from the No. 1 album for guitar and voice, featuring note-for-note tab transcriptions. Includes 'Broken Stones', 'The Changingman', 'Porcelain Gods', 'Out Of The Sinking', 'You Do Something To Me', 'Time Passes...' and 'I Walk On Gilded Splinters'.

Paul Weller - Wild Wood
(Piano/Vocal/Guitar)
Order No. AM91706
Matching folio to the hit album arranged for piano and voice with guitar chord boxes. Includes 'Sunflower', 'Wild Wood', 'The Weaver', 'Foot Of The Mountain' & 'All The Pictures On The Wall'.

Available from your local music dealer or, in case of difficulty, from Music Sales Limited.

Working
on Canvas

Working
on Canvas

Margaret Rivers

B.T. Batsford Ltd, London

First published 1990

ISBN 0 7134 65883

Typeset by Tradespools Ltd., Frome, Somerset
and printed in Hong Kong
for the Publishers
B. T. Batsford Ltd
4 Fitzhardinge Street
London W1H 0AH

Acknowledgement

Thanks are due to all friends and students
who have so generously given their time, or
lent their work for inclusion in this book.
Special thanks to Jim Pascoe for tackling the
photography with unfailing humour, and to
Mrs Anne Woolston who went to so much
trouble to bring me up to date on the
needlework rugs of Portugal; also to Pat Parker
Pearson and Phoebe Kane for permitting me to
use their ideas on rolled fabrics and crochet
respectively, and to Margaret Humphrey who
introduced me to stretching work on a cake
board.

Margaret Rivers

CONTENTS

Introduction 6

ONE *Background* 7

TWO *Equipment and materials* 12

Frames 12; Needles 13; Other tools 13; Canvas 13; Threads 19; Beads, bugles, etc. 25; Found objects, mirror glass, etc. 28

THREE *Making a start and basic techniques* 29

Dressing a frame 29; Starting and finishing 29; Stretching 30; Mounting canvaswork panels 30; Hangings 33; Applying pieces of fabric, leather, etc. 33; Joining canvas 34

FOUR *Stitches for canvaswork* 35

Composite stitches 44; Eyelets 45; Raised stitches 45; Superimposing 45

FIVE *Patterns in canvaswork* 46

Florentine patterns 52; Simulated three-dimensional patterns 55

SIX *Designing for canvaswork* 59

Art materials 59; Ways of arriving at a design 60; Line, shape, form, colour and texture 61; Lettering 64; Three-dimensional items 64; Enlarging and reducing 66; Photocopying 66; Transferring a design on to the canvas 66; Using graph paper to adapt a design to canvas 69

SEVEN *Canvaswork for practical purposes* 70

Decorative panels and wall-hangings 72; Bags and purses 72; Cushions 72; Lamp bases 72; Door stops 73; Small items 73; Garments 73; Belts and buttons 73; Rugs 73; Boxes 74; Book covers 76; Church kneelers 76; Community schemes 76; Simple finishes 76

EIGHT *Experimental canvaswork* 78

Paint, spray and dye 80; Colouring the canvas 80; Changing the stitch 80; Couching 82; Changing the surface 84; Manipulating canvas 85; Cutting 86; Raising the surface 88; Changing the scale 89; Machining on canvas 91; Mixed media 92

Further reading 94

Suppliers 95

Index 96

INTRODUCTION

There is no doubt that canvaswork is one of the most popular embroidery techniques. Stitches are made by counting threads, and perhaps it is this, combined with the regularity of the canvas and the rhythm of the work, which gives confidence even to those who have never stitched before. Many now experienced embroiderers once began with a 'tapestry'* kit.

Examples of historical canvaswork can be seen in museums and in stately homes, often in their original settings. In Britain, some National Trust properties have items on display, and the collections of the Victoria and Albert Museum in London house many examples. The collection of the Embroiderers' Guild (located at Hampton Court Palace) contains modern as well as historical work.

The first part of this book lists equipment and materials and shows how to use them. There are basic vocabularies of stitches and patterns which will enable the beginner to make a start, with suggestions on how these can be developed further. There is also some guidance on planning original designs. The final section introduces some new approaches to canvaswork; these grew out of a curiosity to see whether the bounds of this technique might be widened. The ideas should be treated as starting points and not as ends in themselves.

A list of suppliers appears on p. 95. This is correct at the time of going to press but, to avoid disappointment, it is advisable to get in touch before making a journey of any length. Advertisements giving details of specialist suppliers and their services will be found in magazines such as *Embroidery* and *Crafts*. Suggestions for useful further reading are listed at the end of the book. Some books are now out of print, but should be obtainable by special request through the public library service.

We are now approaching the end of the twentieth century. Canvaswork, together with other arts and crafts, must reflect its own time – it should look forward, building on the past but not reproducing it. An awareness of good design, fitness for purpose and a high standard of technique, allied to an open mind, will lead the embroiderer towards the fun of trying out the exciting new threads and materials on the market today – they are waiting to be explored in the context of canvaswork. That is the underlying purpose of this book and, hopefully, readers will follow the suggested leads and make their own discoveries.

---

* The term 'tapestry', applied to canvaswork, is a misnomer, since true tapestry is woven on a loom and not stitched on a background fabric. Large areas of tent stitch closely resemble woven tapestry and the two words may have become synonymous as early as the sixteenth century, when canvaswork hangings were a good substitute for the more expensive tapestry ones.

CHAPTER 1

BACKGROUND

It is not the intention here to give a complete history of canvaswork, but since the work of today has evolved from that of past centuries, it may not be out of place to include a brief outline of the development of the technique in Britain.

Embroidery dates back thousands of years. Ancient tombs have yielded treasure troves of artefacts, including textiles and embroideries, many worked to an amazingly high standard. The origins of canvaswork are obscure but it has a long history in Europe – mainly in England and France, but also in Spain, Italy and Germany.

Canvas as a background, in the form that we know it today, was introduced during the nineteenth century. Canvaswork *stitches* were originally worked on even-weave linen of

Florentine work. British, early-mid twentieth century (Embroiderers' Guild Collection)

varying counts, i.e. the number of threads to the centimetre/inch. Where flax is grown, spun and woven, the result is even-weave fabric, and stitches made by counting the threads of such a fabric (for example tent stitch and cross stitch) will be even and regular. Even though it has not always been done on canvas, it seems reasonable to assume that canvaswork evolved in this way.

Since the stitches in traditional canvaswork completely cover the background fabric, it is extremely hard-wearing. Throughout the centuries, therefore, it has been used for bags, purses, cushions, hangings, covering furniture, and for any other purpose where hard wear is a consideration. It is probably for this reason that tent and cross stitches have always been popular with embroiderers, as can be seen

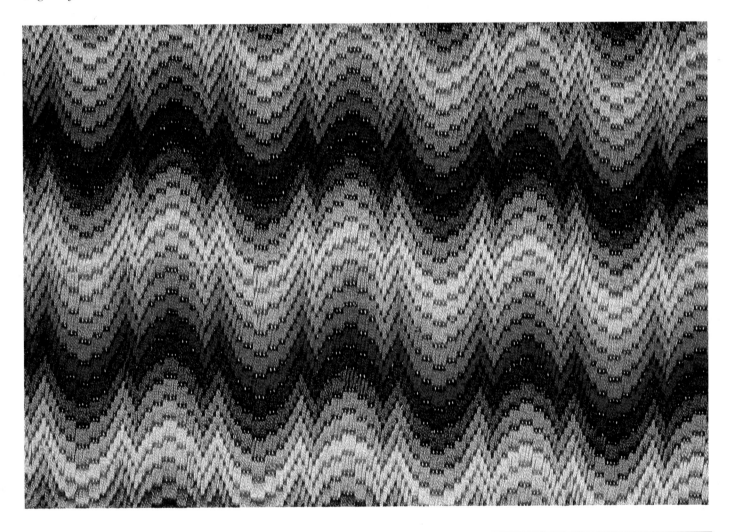

from the evidence of surviving pieces. The fineness of some historical work is almost unbelievable; pieces exist which have hundreds of tent stitches to the square inch.

Tent and cross stitches were not the only ones in use, however. The Hatton Garden hangings, dating from the late seventeenth century and for many years hidden behind layers of wallpaper in an old house in Hatton Garden, London, included rococo, Hungarian and rice stitches, and also some French knots, indicating that contemporary embroiderers were quite ready to include a variety of stitches in a piece of work if it seemed appropriate. The hangings are now housed in the Victoria and Albert Museum.

Fragments of early work have survived from the Middle Ages – a tribute to the work's longevity – but to examine work in any quantity it is necessary to look to the late sixteenth century. The great flowering of embroidery at this time included canvaswork, and despite wear and tear, and dirt and moths, a fair amount of it can still be seen and enjoyed today, although it may take a little imagination to bring the faded colours to life again. The early Elizabethans seem to have shared with the Victorians a passion for decoration; clothes and household furnishings were richly embroidered and canvaswork was popular. Much of the work, particularly large items, came from professional workshops, but a great deal was produced at home. Canvaswork was used not only for small items such as bags and pincushions, but also for larger cushions, bed furniture, table carpets and bed hangings. In the case of the last of these it was an excellent substitute for much more expensive woven tapestries. In the home a big undertaking such as a set of bed hangings would have been the work of several people, probably the mistress of the house assisted by other members of her family and household. Further up the social scale, the joint needlework ventures of Mary Queen of Scots and Bess of Hardwick (at the time when Bess's husband, the Earl of Shrewsbury, was Mary's jailer during her imprisonment in England) are well recorded – and included canvaswork. Mary had her own embroiderer who would have drawn out her designs for her, but more humble people drew out their own designs or used the services of

travelling artists or draughtsmen. Some of Mary's designs were inspired by woodcuts in the herbals and bestiaries available to her; others reflected the contemporary interest in emblems, riddles and allegories. The writings of Margaret Swain and George Wingfield Digby on this subject make fascinating reading (see the bibliography at the end of the book).

Much of the embroidery and canvaswork from this period reflects the Elizabethan interest in gardens and the flowers, fruit and vegetables which grew in them, even including the insects, caterpillars and snails. To avoid the tedium of working endless background, the embroiderers would sometimes work a motif such as a plant, animal or bird, or even a small picture, and then cut it out and apply it to a fabric background, usually velvet. This would have been a much quicker way of producing large furnishings like bed curtains, and had the added advantage that when the background wore out the motifs could be transferred to a new background. These motifs were called 'slips', a gardener's term adopted by embroiderers, probably because any plants depicted usually had their stems cut off diagonally, as a gardener takes a slip from a plant. Sets of 'slips' could be bought drawn out on linen, ready for embroidery.

Canvaswork pictures first appeared in the seventeenth century. The subjects were mostly biblical or mythical and it was customary to show the figures wearing contemporary dress, so that many a biblical character or Greek goddess bears a startling resemblance to Queen Henrietta Maria.

The Hatton Garden hangings of the late seventeenth century have already been mentioned. A splendid example of early eighteenth century canvaswork can be seen at Aston Hall, Birmingham, where in Lady Mary Holte's room there are two huge canvaswork wall hangings (resembling tapestries) and a large needlework carpet on the floor. One of the hangings bears the date 1744 and the name of Lady Mary Holte; legend has it that she was responsible for all this needlework, but in view of the size of the pieces it would seem likely that others were involved. Possibly she masterminded the operation. The style of the carpet and the hangings is typical of the work of the late seventeenth century. Lady Mary was 60 years of age in 1744 and she probably worked in the idiom of her youth. In any case the hangings and the carpet would have been some considerable time in the making. The room also contains two wing chairs covered in canvaswork, attributed to the same embroiderer.

The eighteenth century has been described as the century of upholstered furniture, which had begun to develop in the 1600s. Sets of chairs, settees, stools and screens, among other things, were covered in fabric, much of it embroidered, or in canvaswork. The latter used woollen threads, the highlights sometimes being picked out in silk. Floral designs were still popular but became much lighter in style than those of the previous century, and many reflected the interest in all things oriental. Florentine patterns were also used as well as pictorial scenes with a Watteau-like character. Small items such as purses and pocket-books were worked more finely, in silks, rather than wool, often in delightful patterns.

Canvaswork was at a peak during this period but, as so often happens, after the high came a low. Quite early in the nineteenth century coloured (and later printed) charts for canvaswork began to appear, originating from Germany, as did the worsted wool in bright colours which gave 'Berlin woolwork' its name. Each square on the chart represented a stitch (usually cross stitch) and the colour indicated the colour of the thread to be used, thus effectively removing any need for initiative from the embroiderer unless she had a mind or ideas of her own. Berlin woolwork was slow to take off at first, but once it did it swept across England, and America. Servants were cheap and many women had time on their hands which they filled with this and other 'fancy work'. At the same time more and more charts were flooding the market, along with the materials to execute them.

At first many of the designs were charming, but as the work became more and more fashionable its quality often deteriorated and the subjects of many of the designs produced were sentimental and even mawkish. Painted canvases ready for working appeared, copied from the work of contemporary painters; Landseer's *Stag at Bay* and other animal pictures were extremely popular, as were illustrations from the novels of Sir Walter Scott.

The introduction in the 1850s of chemical dyes with their hard, garish colours, did nothing to improve the standard of the work.

The Victorian lady's passion for 'fancy work' led her to try many different materials, including beads. These often appear on canvaswork of the middle of the century, with or without stitchery in wool or silk. The 'grisaille' beadwork carried out on canvas, with black, white and grey beads, could be very attractive, with its restrained colour against a background of red or other coloured wool. Many delightful pieces were produced, but much of the work was heavy and – to our eyes – tasteless.

Another variation on canvaswork was 'plushwork'. Parts of the design were raised by using plush stitch and a soft woollen yarn. The stitch itself was not dissimilar to velvet stitch, and a gauge was used to make the loops on the surface of the work. After working, the loops were cut and required areas would then be trimmed and shaped with scissors to make them three-dimensional. To ensure that the stitches did not pull out when cut, it was essential to paste the back of the work. Many a realistic cabbage, rose or parrot was produced by this method. The Embroiderers' Guild possesses a Berlin woolwork sampler on which there sits a magnificent blue budgerigar, more or less life-size. A modern interpretation of this method was given by Diana Springall in the late 1970s, for parts of the large canvaswork panels which she designed for the Town Hall in Chester. These were stitched by 300 local needlewomen, and the use of the raised stitch concealed the fact that so many different hands had been at work – an ingenious solution.

Late nineteenth-century ladies' magazines included canvaswork patterns for slippers, smoking caps, firescreens, stool-tops, bell-pulls, watch pockets, purses and bags *ad infinitum*. The cluttered Victorian interior lent itself to decoration in all forms, including canvaswork.

Everything comes to an end, and Berlin woolwork eventually gave way to art needlework, following the influence of William Morris. Magazines continued to include instructions for canvaswork, however, which indicates that it remained popular with many needlewomen. There are references in

1. Victorian plushwork with beads, showing the flowers in low relief (Embroiderers' Guild Collection)

needlework magazines around the turn of the century to 'canvas braiding' and 'ivory' or 'congress' work. Canvas braiding used a fairly fine canvas or an even-weave linen, on which a braid or coarse thread was tacked down in geometric patterns along the warp or weft of the background; the braid or thread was then attached to the background by means of straight, regular stitches passing through the holes of the canvas, which allowed the braid to show between them. The rest of the background was not stitched. The braid gave the patterns a raised appearance, and it was

recommended that it should match the colour of the canvas as far as possible and that the upper or sewing thread should be in a strong contrasting colour so that it could be seen.

'Congress' appears to refer to a single thread canvas which could be either fine or coarse, depending on the use for which it was intended. Geometric patterns in satin stitch were worked upon it in tones of one colour. Today in the United States, 'congress canvas' appears to be the name of a fine canvas, not heavily-sized, softer than most, and obtainable in a range of colours.

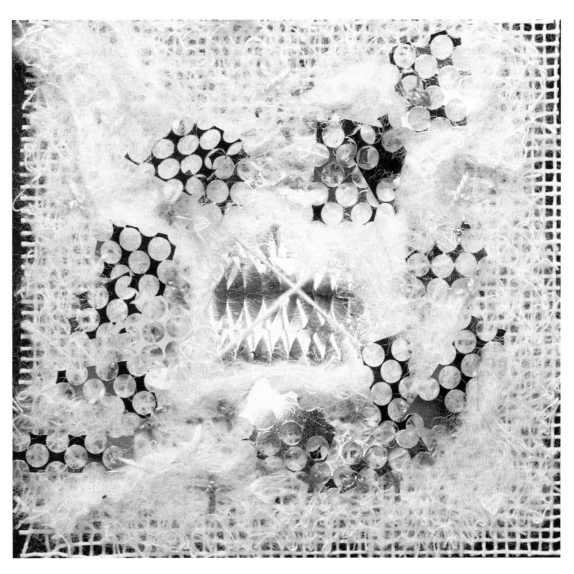

2. Experimental sample, 10 cm (4 in) square, worked on cotton canvas, 12 threads to 2.5 cm (1 in), using domette, scraps of sequin waste and opalescent plastic film combined with free cross stitches (Elizabeth Ashurst)

Many embroiderers have found canvaswork relaxing to work, and this was exploited during the First World War when it was used as a therapy for shell-shocked soldiers.

In common with embroidery generally, canvaswork declined between the two World Wars. Although some very good work was produced at this time, commercial designs were generally poor and there was little stitch variety. Signs of improvement and fresh thinking can be detected in the late 1930s through the influence of artists and embroiderers of the calibre of Mary Hogarth, Claude Flight, Aileen Booker and Rosamund Willis, but rationing and shortage of materials in the years during and immediately following the Second World War – plus the fact that many women were serving in the Armed Forces or the factories, or giving voluntary service – created a hiatus during which little embroidery was produced, although it must

be stated that some women contrived to produce beautiful work with their limited materials, helped by an abundant supply of patience and ingenuity.

Peacetime saw a gradual resumption of interest in all kinds of embroidery and canvaswork. This has escalated since the 1950s and continues to do so today. There is also an increasing awareness of the need for good design, allied to technical excellence, if the craft is to progress into the twenty-first century. The popularity of City and Guilds courses in embroidery and the proliferation of Embroiderers' Guild branches has led to many embroiderers seeking to expand the horizons of embroidery as a whole and using it as a means of personal expression. This in turn has led to the production of much experimental work, although there is still room for traditional and practical kinds of canvaswork.

CHAPTER 2

EQUIPMENT *and* MATERIALS

Buy the best you can afford. It always pays.

Equipment

FRAMES

It is sometimes convenient to work a small piece in the hand, but anything larger than 15–20 cm (6–8 in) in any direction needs to be mounted in a frame, to avoid distortion caused by the diagonal 'pull' of many canvaswork stitches. Once distortion occurs it is often difficult, and sometimes impossible, to correct. A piece worked in Florentine stitch might be an exception to this rule, but the use of a frame will not only avoid distortion to a very large extent, but will also help to keep the tension of the stitches even, leading to a better finish.

Some people dislike working with a frame but the majority find that with practice its use is an advantage. If the frame has a stand, or can be balanced between two tables or chair-backs, both hands can be brought into use (one above and one below the canvas), and the work will progress more rapidly. This skill is well worth acquiring.

The frame may be a rectangular embroidery frame (slate frame), which may or may not have a floor stand. If it does not, it can be rested against a table or chairs as described above. A simple wooden frame, to which the canvas can be stapled or tacked, can be made at home. Alternatively, picture stretchers of the kind used by artists to stretch their canvas, obtainable from suppliers of art materials, can be used. Even an old wooden picture frame can be pressed into service if nothing else is available and the wood is soft enough to allow drawing pins to penetrate. Instructions for dressing these frames are given in the next chapter.

Generally speaking, a tambour frame (ring frame) is not recommended for canvaswork, as the canvas cannot be stretched tightly enough and the ring will mark the work. A way round this is to stretch a piece of firm fabric, such as strong calico, in the ring frame and tack the canvas to it, keeping the canvas square to the grain of the fabric. The canvas is then worked in the usual way, taking the stitches through the backing fabric as well as the canvas. When the work is finished, the surplus backing fabric can be cut away or left to form a 'frame' for the canvaswork. The edges of interlocked canvas

used in this way do not unravel, but ordinary canvas can be frayed out deliberately. Woollen threads tend to wear thin quickly using this method, so only short lengths should be used.

Breaking with tradition, a piece of canvas can be placed on top of a larger piece of tweed, silk, velvet or corduroy, and the stitches taken through both as with the calico. The surplus fabric surrounding the canvas becomes a ready-made mount when the work is finished. The edges of the canvas can be stitched over to make a decorative border, or left as the design dictates.

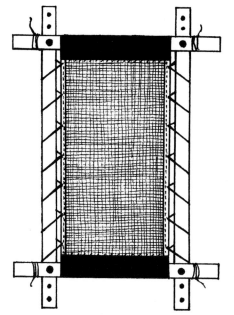 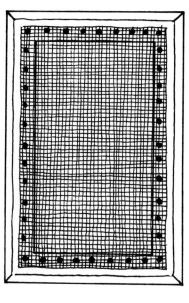

3. *(Left) Slate frame mounted with canvas ready for working (Right) Method of mounting canvas on a frame made from a picture stretcher or an old picture frame. A similar frame could be made at home*

Another alternative is to machine stitch the piece of canvas firmly to a larger piece of calico or similar firm fabric, then cut away the fabric behind the canvas and mount the whole in a ring frame for working. These methods are useful when travelling, or at times when a rectangular frame is a nuisance. They are quite satisfactory for small pieces of work or samples.

If small pieces are worked in the hand, it may be necessary to overcast or bind the edges to avoid fraying, and threads catching in the edge of the canvas; this can be most irritating, besides snagging the thread. Masking tape, obtainable from stationers and art suppliers, is useful for this.

NEEDLES

Tapestry needles are used for canvaswork. Blunt, to avoid splitting the threads of the canvas, and with a long eye, they come in a range of sizes (mixed packets are available) and should be selected so that the eye takes the thread easily, and both needle and thread pass through the canvas without tugging.

For work on rug canvas, particularly when using strips of torn fabric, the type of needle used by knitters to sew up seams and run in ends of yarn is useful. These needles are also blunt and have long eyes, but are much larger than the largest tapestry needle.

Also obtainable are curved needles made for upholstery and other repair work. They are sometimes easier to use than a straight needle when making up three-dimensional pieces or attaching objects to a surface.

OTHER TOOLS

Apart from needles, **embroidery scissors** and a large pair of **sharp scissors for cutting canvas** will be necessary. Some people claim not to be able to use a **thimble**, but it is a habit worth acquiring as canvaswork can be tough on the fingers at times. If working two-handed, a thimble on each hand may be desirable. **Small tweezers** can be a great help when unpicking stitches.

Materials

CANVAS

Basically there are two kinds of canvas, usually made from linen or cotton, but some mixed fibre canvases and also a jute canvas, are available. Linen canvas is the most expensive, but is the hardest wearing and therefore advisable for any work where this has to be considered. **Single thread or 'Mono' canvas** is pleasant to use and more versatile than double thread canvas, which distorts some stitches, thus restricting choice. Some single thread canvases are described as 'interlocking' or 'interlocked', i.e. the threads in one direction are twisted at the intersection, so that the canvas does not ravel easily. This is useful for experimental work. Alternative names for this kind of canvas are 'lockweave' or 'Leno'.

Double thread canvas, also known as 'Penelope' canvas, first appeared in the second quarter of the nineteenth century. It is the most suitable for trammed work, and the double threads can be 'pricked' so that areas of fine stitchery can be combined with coarser stitches in the same piece (see 'Changing the Scale'). Both types of canvas come in a range of sizes, identified by counting the number of threads or holes to the centimetre or inch. The sizes range from 10 to 32 threads to 2.5 cm (1 in). *N.B. Stitches are worked by counting threads not holes.*

When choosing canvas, consider the purpose for which it is to be used. Will it receive hard wear? Can the worker stitch it without eyestrain? Consider also the scale of the canvas in relation to the finished article – a coarse canvas would not be suitable for a small article like a spectacle case or purse.

Rug canvas may have 3, 4 or 5 holes to 2.5 cm (1 in) and, apart from its obvious use for rugs, lends itself to other applications, particularly large wall hangings and experimental work. **Rya canvas**, intended for making the shaggy Finnish-style rugs, also has possibilities for experiments.

Obtainable from specialist suppliers is a single thread **raffia canvas**, buff-coloured and approximately 10 threads to 2.5 cm (1 in). Not all the sizes of canvas referred to will be stocked by local shops, who tend to carry two or three sizes in the middle of the range. Only specialist embroidery suppliers have the full range, but their mail order service is generally good. Advertisements can be found in magazines such as *Embroidery*.

Silk gauze, at the opposite end of the scale to rug canvas, is extremely fine and is now very expensive. It is only stocked by a few specialist suppliers. **Waste canvas** comes in single or double thread and this can also be obtained from specialist suppliers. Its prime purpose is to facilitate the working of cross stitch (and other stitches normally worked on an even-weave background) on a non-even-weave background. The waste canvas is laid on top of the background fabric and the stitches are worked through both canvas and background fabric; when the stitching is complete the work is moistened slightly and the threads of the canvas can be withdrawn, leaving the stitches intact on the background.

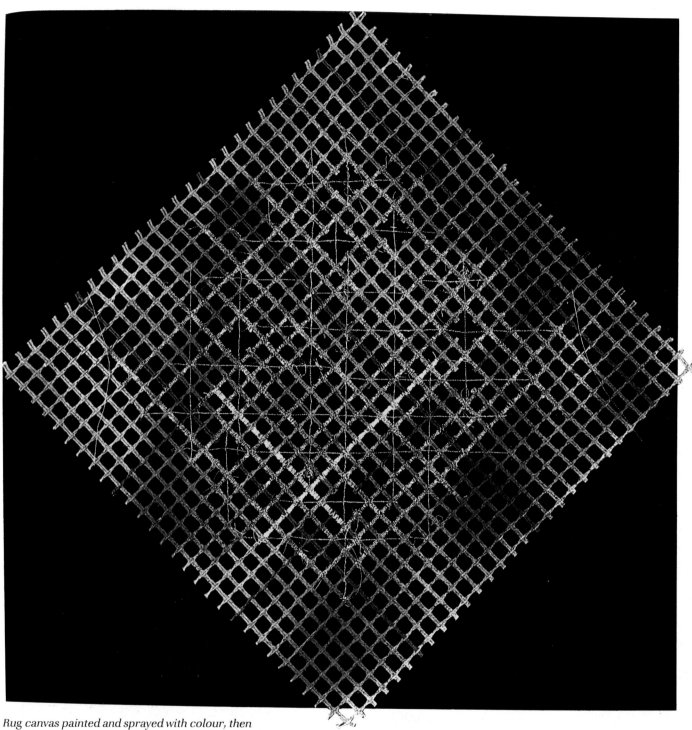

Rug canvas painted and sprayed with colour, then
machine whipped, mainly with metallic threads.
Some areas have been cut away (Alana Coombes)

4. (Opposite) (Top, left to right) Single thread canvas,
double thread canvas, interlocked canvas. (Centre,
left to right) Rug canvas, rya rug canvas, 'waste'
canvas. (Bottom, left to right) Net with diamond
mesh, nylon mesh, metal mesh

5. Rya canvas painted with metallic paint and darned with soft silk twisted threads and torn strips of chiffon and organza, with some buttonhole and cross stitches (Margaret Rivers)

6. Detail of fine canvaswork on silk gauze. Chinese, possibly early twentieth century (Embroiderers' Guild Collection)

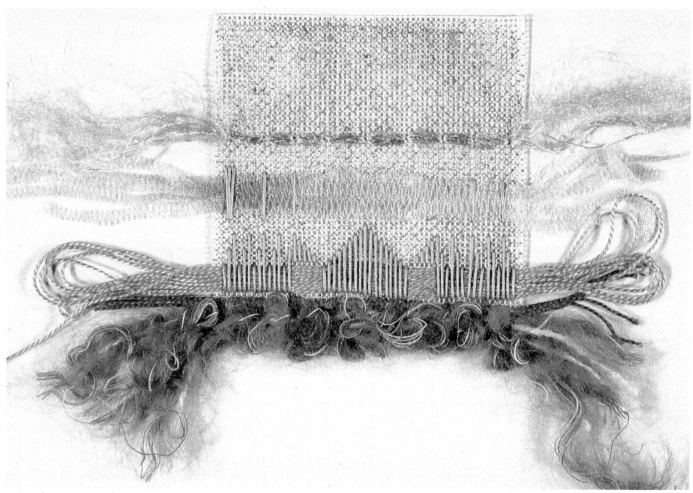

*Painted canvas sample
with applied and
couched threads,
including tubular
knitting yarn (Lesley
Barnett)*

A coarse **linen scrim** (also known as 'Winchester canvas') is not as stiff as ordinary canvas and is useful for rugs and kneelers as it is easy to manipulate and make up.

There are some alternatives to canvas made with natural fibres. **Plastic 'canvas'** is rigid and comes in various counts and colours. It is stocked by some needlework and craft shops and is particularly suitable for box-making and other three-dimensional work, as the sections can be 'thonged' together quite easily. Circular pieces, obtainable in various sizes, are useful for making the bottoms and lids of boxes, or for mobiles, etc. The rigidity of this canvas means that it can be worked in the hand, but the finished work has a quite different quality to that of ordinary canvas, and not everyone finds this appealing. **Plastic mesh** vegetable bags, plastic-covered garden mesh, and other plastic meshes used in industry and the building trade, can be used for experiments. It is worth keeping a look-out for these in do-it-yourself shops. Stiff nets and gauzes can be found; some have a diamond-shaped mesh.

Some interesting and imaginative work has been produced (notably by Helen Pincus) using *metal mesh* from motor accessory shops and, although it is not 'canvas' in the strictest sense, any mesh or grid can be considered as a basis for stitches, and may suggest other approaches such as wrapping, knotting or tying. Some inventive work has been done with chicken wire. On a large scale torn strips of fabric, string, cord, etc., can be used as substitutes for thread. The possibilities are endless. There is an instance of a student who covered her garden trellis with canvaswork stitches using thick string for thread.

THREADS

Traditional threads for canvaswork include **crewel wool** (2-ply), **tapestry wool** (4-ply) and **silk**. Of these, crewel wool is the most useful as the number of strands can be varied to suit the canvas, the stitch and the work in hand. Tapestry wool is slightly more limited in its application, but both come in excellent ranges of colours from various manufacturers, and most are colourfast and moth-proof. Some are washable, which will be marked on the wrapper.

Silk threads come in different thicknesses and the twisted ones are the most comfortable to use with canvas. In the past silk was often used to highlight a piece of work or for very fine work on silk gauze, and there are some outstanding Chinese examples of the latter.

Other threads include **coton perlé (pearl cotton)**, **stranded cotton**, **coton à broder** (a single thread which is the equivalent of four strands of stranded cotton), **soft embroidery** thread and **crochet cotton**. Raffia, knitting yarns, cords, string, even lengths of tubular french knitting, can all be used as 'alternative' threads, and inventive embroiders will be able to think of others, but it is advisable to work small samples on oddments of canvas to find out how these 'threads' react to being passed through the canvas a number of times. Some results may be disappointing, but others will be surprisingly effective. Knobbly threads, such as bouclé, which are difficult or impossible to pull through the canvas, can be couched down, either on top of solid areas of other stitchery or directly on to the canvas itself.

The narrow **ribbons** currently on the market can be used as 'thread' on large-gauge canvases, and contrast well with wool and cotton threads. Wider ribbons lend themselves to use with rug canvas, as do strips of torn fabric. Torn silk is particularly effective, the frayed edges of the strips making a pleasing texture. Silk, woollen or cotton prints used in this way introduce some interesting colour and pattern variations, and knitted fabrics (stocking stitch) curl up at the edges, giving the strips the appearance of rouleaux. Felt, leather and suede strips are other possibilities. It is worth trying out all sorts of things.

Some metallic knitting yarns work well on canvas, but traditional metal threads must be laid on the surface and couched. Metal purls can be sewn down in much the same way as bugle beads. However, it is not easy to achieve a worthwhile effect using metallic threads on canvas (metallic machine embroidery threads are an exception), possibly because they do not seem to integrate easily with the surface. This is an area which may well reward further exploration.

It is worth building up a varied collection of threads. Contrast is an important element in all embroidery, and having an assortment to choose from makes for lively canvaswork.

7. (Above) Sample worked with synthetic raffia and sparkly tubular thread on plastic canvas. Embroidery 75 cm (3 in) square. The rigidity of the canvas can be clearly seen (Margaret Rivers)

8. (Right) Detail from panel 'Ritenuto' by Helen Pincus. Worked on metal mesh with metallic threads and random-dyed braid; partly stitched and partly couched. Wrapped rods are superimposed

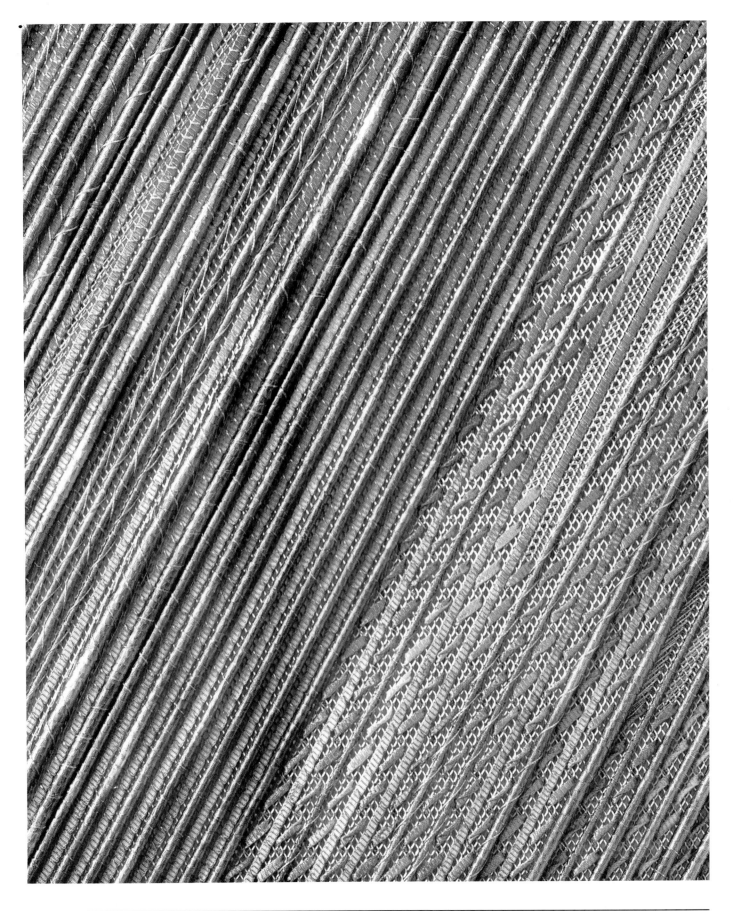

9. *Stitch sample in natural raffia on rug canvas, 8 threads to 2.5 cm (1 in) (Vicky Lugg)*

10. Vertical gobelin stitch worked in a free form to suggest clumps of plants in a herbaceous border. Threads range in thickness from stranded cotton to tubular knitting yarn and strips of coloured tights (Ruth Collins)

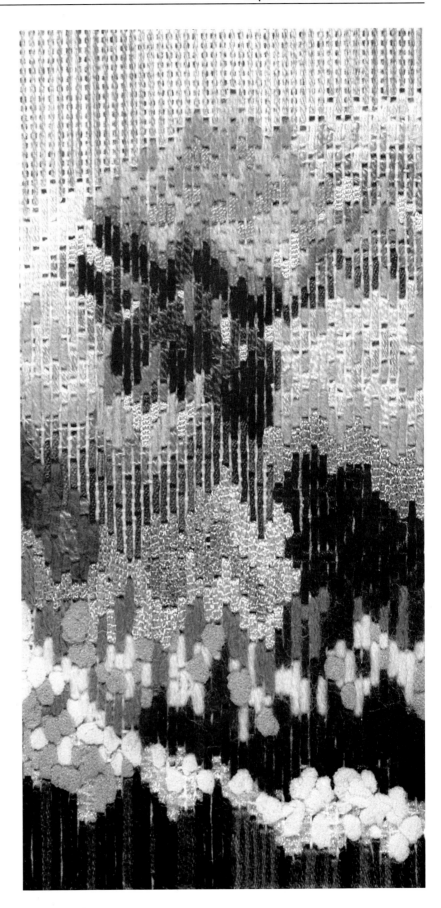

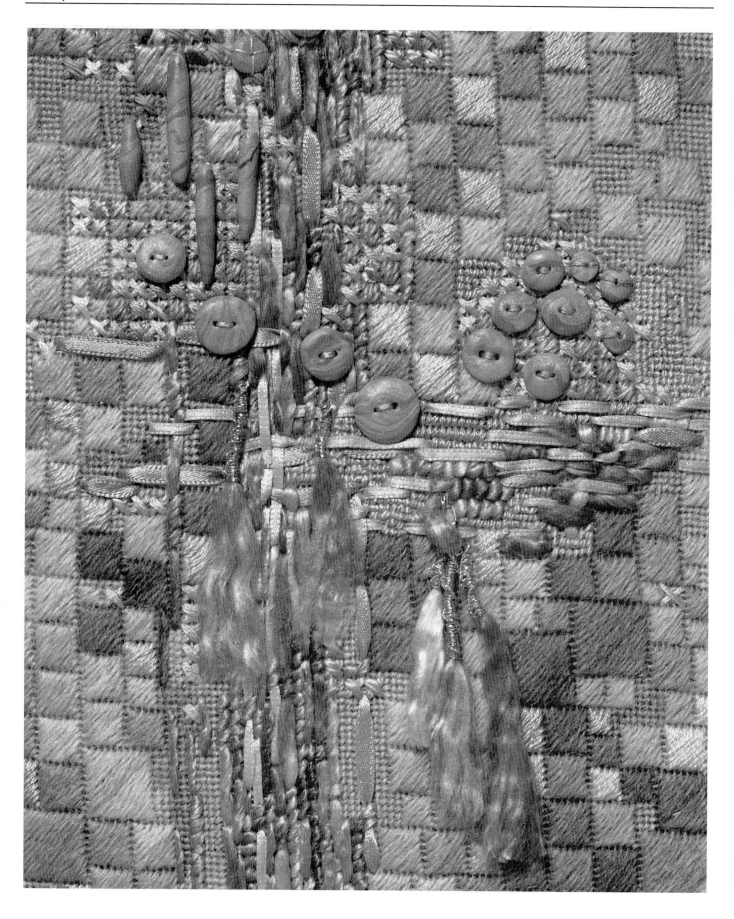

11. (Left) Imaginative use of canvas stitches and silk threads, combined with narrow ribbon used as a thread, and hand-made beads and buttons (Muriel Best)

12. (Right) Various methods of attaching beads and bugles to canvas

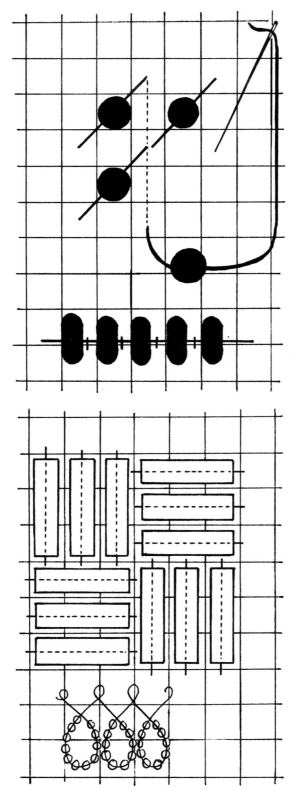

BEADS, BUGLES, ETC.

Beads can be used on canvas, either on their own or combined with wool or other stitchery. Because of their weight, beads must be sewn down very securely – two stitches, or even three, in each bead are better than one – which makes the work slow, but to balance this, beads usually retain their colour and are fairly easy to clean.

Choose beads of a size which will make them lie close together on the canvas when the work is finished. Single or double canvas can be used, providing the beads are the right size. Use a strong silk thread, which should be rubbed on beeswax, and a fine needle; long, thin needles called 'beading needles' are obtainable from haberdashery counters. Occasionally these are referred to as 'straw' or 'milliner's' needles.

It is important to make sure that the thread is very secure when starting work and also when finishing off. As can be seen in figure 12, the beads are attached with a diagonal stitch over two threads of the canvas. Another method of attaching beads is by threading several at one time on to a single thread and couching them down at intervals. This practice is sometimes frowned upon, but it has some decorative possibilities for those who are interested in more experimental work. For instance, loops of beads can be left hanging here and there. Bugle beads (the tube-like ones) can also be sewn on to canvas and are effective when used in blocks.

Single beads, bugles, sequins and spangles can be sewn into a surface of canvaswork stitches where required. If single beads are sewn on to unworked canvas at intervals, each will need to be fastened off separately; if the thread is taken across the back of the canvas between the beads it will be seen from the right side, unless it is hidden by stitching the canvas.

13. Sample of raised beadwork with tent stitch on canvas, by Valentina Brun (Embroiderers' Guild Collection)

Panel, approximately 200 cm (8 in) square, one of a series 'Precious Gardens', by Vicky Lugg. Rice and cushion stitch worked over gauze-covered canvas. Threads vary in weight from perlé and silk twist to coton à broder and stranded cotton

FOUND OBJECTS, MIRROR GLASS, ETC.

These can also be attached to canvas or superimposed on an area of stitchery. One way to attach such objects is to take long stitches right across them, and these can form part of a design. An alternative is to outline the object in buttonhole stitch with the 'leg' part of the stitch pointing inwards or outwards as wished; using *detached* buttonhole stitch, or detached knotted buttonhole stitch, work into the loops of the buttonhole stitches to make a small 'pocket' to hold the object securely. You will need to hold the object in position while working in order to shape the pocket correctly.

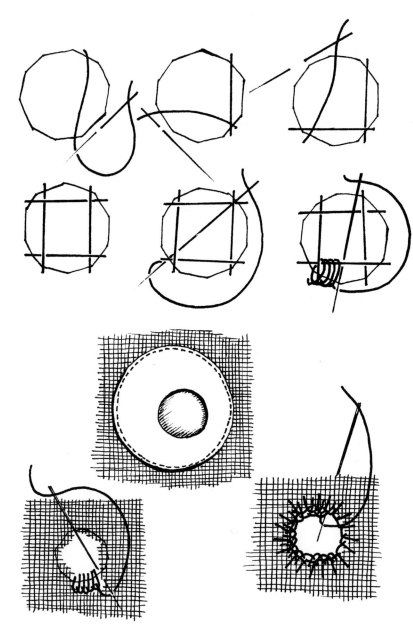

14. Ways of attaching objects to canvas. (Top) A similar method to that used when attaching shisha glass. (Centre) Non-fray material, such as leather, has a suitably-sized hole cut in it to allow the object to be seen, and at the same time holds it firmly in place. (Bottom left) A hole is cut in the canvas and the edge buttonholed to neaten and strengthen it. (Bottom right) A hole is cut in the canvas and neatened with a row of buttonhole stitch, worked with the 'legs' pointing outwards. Detached buttonhole stitch is then worked into the loops for as many rows as necessary to trap the object underneath. The last two methods will require a backing to keep the object in place

CHAPTER 3

MAKING A START *and* BASIC TECHNIQUES

The reasons for using a frame for canvaswork have already been explained. It is sufficient to repeat that working with a frame helps to achieve an even tension, and avoids distortion of the canvas which may be difficult to correct.

Dressing a frame

A slate (rectangular) frame consists of two rollers, each with a strip of webbing attached to it, and two slats which slot into the rollers to form a rectangle. The maximum *width* of canvas which can be mounted in a particular frame is governed by the length of the webbing, e.g. 30 cm (12 in), but any surplus *length* of canvas can be rolled round one or both rollers, the work being adjusted as it progresses. Note that if the canvas is rolled it will not be quite as taut as when it is fully stretched.

Before using a slate frame for the first time, mark the exact centre of each strip of webbing with an indelible pen. Machine stitch, or stitch firmly by hand, a length of strong tape approximately 2.5 cm (1 in) wide along each side of the canvas to be mounted. Mark accurately the centre of each end of the canvas, then, matching the marks, place the right side of one end of the canvas to the right side of the strip of webbing on one roller; overcast firmly together with small stitches, working out from the centre in both directions. Repeat this operation with the other end of the canvas and the other roller. Now roll any surplus canvas round the roller, adjust so that the canvas is as taut as possible, and place the pegs or clips provided in position to hold the frame together. With thin string, or a strong thread which does not stretch, lace the sides of the canvas to the slats as shown in figure 3 (page 12), finishing by knotting the string round the frame to secure it. The canvas should now be very taut, with the warp and weft threads correctly aligned at right angles to each other. As the work progresses it will probably be necessary to adjust the canvas – it may have become slack, or it will need moving along. In either case, remove the lacing, make the necessary adjustments and then replace the lacing.

If canvas is to be mounted on a home-made rectangular frame or one made from artists' stretchers, proceed in exactly the same way as is described under 'Stretching' below. Masking tape over the heads of the pins and the edges of the canvas will prevent the thread from snagging.

Starting and finishing

Are you sitting comfortably? This question is not as frivolous as it sounds. Many embroiderers give themselves a crick in the neck or a backache because their posture is bad, or because they are sitting on a chair which is too low or too high. Try to ensure that your back is well supported and you do not sit in a hunched position for hours on end. If you are comfortable your embroidery will be that much more enjoyable.

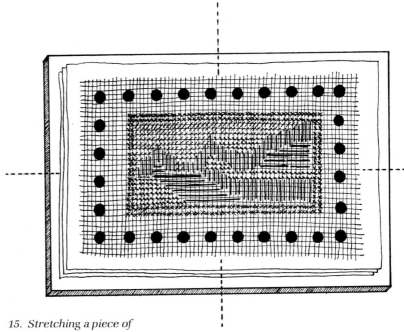

15. Stretching a piece of finished work

TO BEGIN WORK

Make a strong knot in the end of the thread and take the needle through from the front to the back of the canvas, a short distance from the first stitch, so that as the stitching progresses the thread at the back of the work will be covered and held in place. When it is secure, cut off the knot and run in any surplus thread at the back of the stitches. Finish off in the same way by taking the thread through to the back of the work and running it through the back of the completed stitches. Do not be tempted to start with a knot at the back of the work – it may make an ugly lump on the front of the finished piece.

It is also very tempting to use a long thread to sew with, but for canvaswork particularly this is not advisable; the thread wears thin after it has passed through the canvas a number of times, and this shows up quite badly on the right side, spoiling the appearance of the work.

STRETCHING

If a frame has been used it will probably not be necessary to stretch the work when completed, but if any distortion has occurred, or the stitching is not as even as it might be, then stretching may help to solve the problem.

On a wooden board (a drawing board can be used), larger than the piece to be stretched, place several layers of newspaper, plus one or two layers of white blotting paper on top; then damp them thoroughly. The piece of canvaswork goes on top again, face upwards. Using rustproof drawing pins, tacks or staples, and starting in the centre at the top, work out in both directions, pinning as you go. Note that the pins should be fairly close together. Pin the bottom in the same way, slightly tensioning the canvas so that the vertical threads are quite straight. Now pin out the two sides, checking that the vertical and horizontal threads are really squared up and the work is its correct shape – if necessary, measure it to make sure. At this stage do not worry if there is some puckering. Leave at room temperature for two or three days until everything is quite dry, then remove the pins, and all should be well. Very occasionally it may be necessary to repeat the process, but this is exceptional if care has been taken to follow the rules from the beginning.

For small pieces a cake board (the silver kind used for Christmas and wedding cakes, and stocked by stationers) can be used for stretching very successfully.

MOUNTING CANVASWORK PANELS

The way a piece of work is mounted is very much a personal decision, and will be influenced by such factors as the environment in which it will be displayed, whether it is a commissioned piece, the cost and your experience. Work on finer canvases can be laced over strong card before being placed in a frame; its apearance can be improved by placing a piece of felt, the same size as the card, behind the canvaswork. Plastic foam is sometimes used as a substitute for felt, but its life is limited and it will eventually disintegrate. Whether the mounted and framed work should be glazed or not is a matter of personal choice; although glazing detracts from the tactile quality of textiles, many people feel that it gives protection from dirt. Framers sometimes suggest the use of non-reflecting glass, but this has a rather dead quality which many people dislike.

A conventional card mount to frame the piece is reasonably easy to cut using a craft knife and a metal ruler. Card mounts look much better if cut with a bevelled edge, and it is possible to buy gadgets in do-it-yourself shops which help with this, but it may be simpler to buy a ready-cut mount from a framing shop, as you do need to practise using these tools to achieve successful results.

Another idea is to stretch the work over card, as above, and mount it on to a large piece of fabric-covered card. To secure it attach string or very strong thread at suitable places on the back of the mounted piece (usually at the corners) and pierce holes at corresponding points through the larger mount; take the strings through the holes to the back, and fasten securely. Alternatively, if the smaller mount is not too heavy, it can be stitched to the larger one using a curved needle. Two textile surfaces marry well together, and canvaswork is enhanced if the surrounding mount is covered with fabric; velvet and corduroy are very successful foils to canvaswork, as are leather and suede.

If possible, always use acid-free card for mounting, otherwise the embroidery may suffer in the course of time. Hardboard can also be used, and a layer of acid-free paper placed between it and the embroidery.

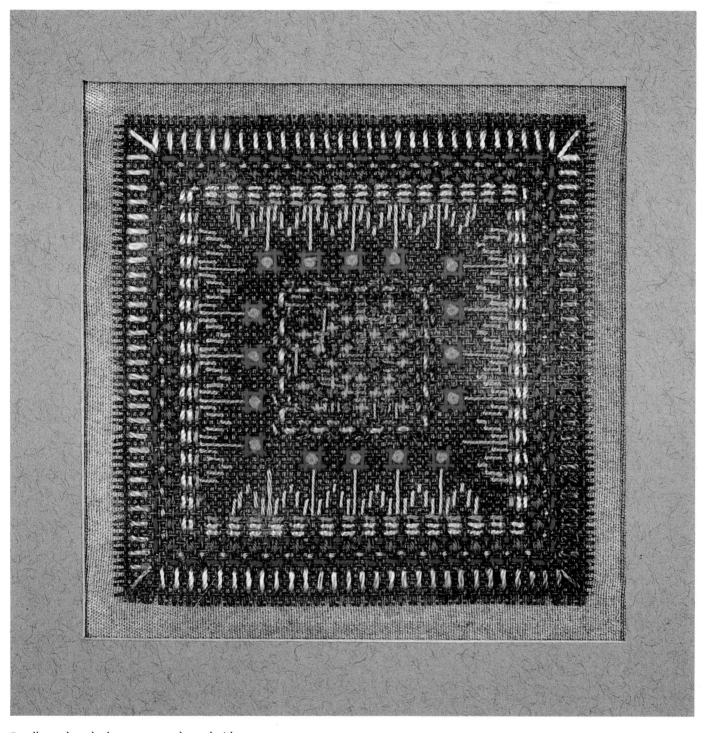

Small panel worked on canvas, coloured with green ink and worked almost entirely in straight stitches with silk threads. The design is based on a formal garden (Margaret Rivers)

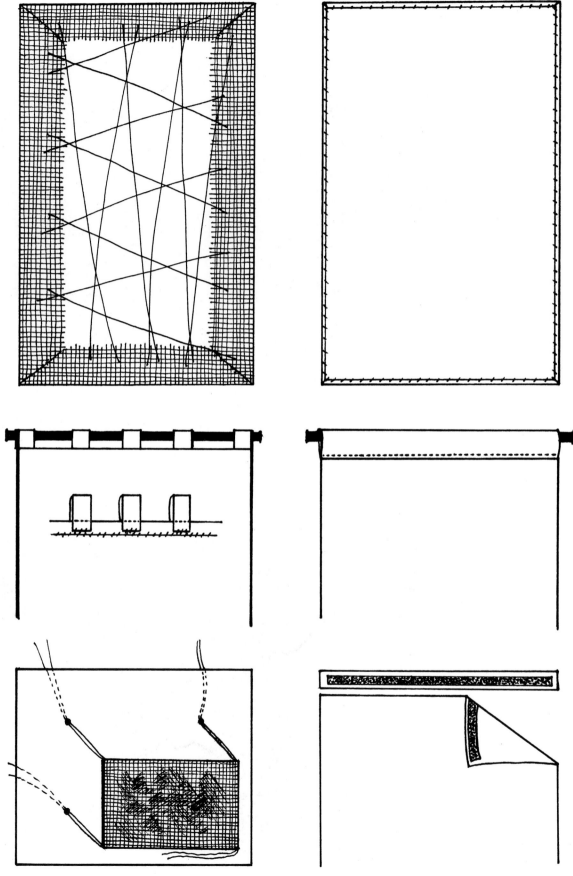

16. Methods of mounting and hanging work. (Top left) Canvas wrapped round thick card or board and laced to hold it in position. (Top right) Back of work neatened with a piece of fabric stitched in place. (Centre left) Soft hanging suspended by loops with method of attaching loops shown below. (Centre right) Simple wide hem with rod passed through it. (Bottom left) Attaching a stiffly mounted piece to another mount. (Bottom right) Attaching a soft hanging to a batten by means of Velcro

Hangings

If canvaswork is to be mounted as a soft hanging, it will need to be lined with pelmet-weight interfacing, heavy-weight calico or linen duck, cut to the size of the finished hanging. The surplus canvas is turned in over the interlining like a hem; the back is then finished with a lining of calico, or other fabric, which is hemmed down to the turnings, thus neatening the back. At this stage consideration will have to be given to the means of hanging – by curtain rings sewn at intervals along the top edge, through which a cane or length of dowelling can be passed; by Velcro, one side stitched along the top of the hanging, and the other stapled or tacked to a batten, with screw eyes at the ends so that it can be suspended from a cord; or by a variation on one of these methods.

Of course these are not the only ways to mount canvaswork. There are many other possibilities. Mounting and framing embroidery of all kinds can present problems, but advance planning will eliminate at least some of them. Try to think of the work and the way it is to be mounted and/or framed as a whole. From the beginning, think through the stages of the work and anticipate what the difficulties might be. This will solve many problems before they arise. At exhibitions, observe how work is mounted, and analyse why one thing is successful but another is not.

APPLYING PIECES OF FABRIC, LEATHER, ETC.

Contrasting one texture against another is an important element in all embroidery. Fabrics such as tweed, velvet, corduroy and leather look well combined with canvaswork. Leather and suede, which do not fray, can be sewn on to canvas with a stab stitch, or on to a surface of canvas stitchery, quite easily. Using a cotton or silk thread, bring the needle up through the canvas and take it down into the piece to be applied; use small straight stitches at regular intervals. Felt is also easy to apply in this way. Applied materials can be raised slightly by padding them with felt or wadding.

Small pieces of fabric can be scattered at random over the canvas and stitched into with formal canvaswork stitches; if some of the fabric is allowed to show between the stitches, interesting surfaces can be created.

A fabric which frays can be laced or wrapped around pelmet-weight interfacing or

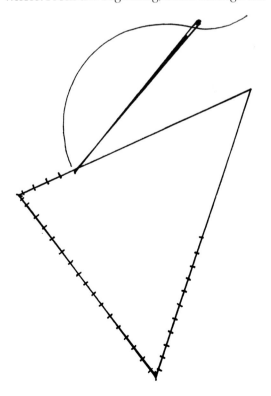
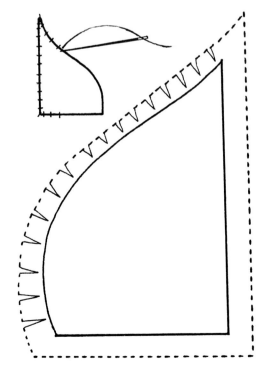

17. Applying pieces of fabric, felt or leather to a background. On the right, snipping a curved edge so that it will lie flat when turned under

card cut to the required shape, and then applied; this method gives sharper edges and looks more professional, but whichever method is used it is usually easier to stitch the canvas first, taking a few extra stitches inside the area to be covered by the applied piece. This prevents the threads of the canvas showing at the join.

JOINING CANVAS

For a large wall-hanging or something similar, or for a three-dimensional shape, it may be necessary to join pieces of canvas together. Here are two ways of doing this:

1 Embroider the canvas to within 1 cm (³/₈ in) of the seam line; put the two pieces of worked canvas face to face, and machine or back stitch along the seam line, making quite sure that the threads of the canvas match, and the right side has the appearance of one piece of canvas. Continue embroidering over the seam – but *not* through the turnings which would make a ridge in the work. The result should be an invisible join.

2 Embroider the canvas to within 1 cm (³/₈ in) of the seam on both pieces of canvas to be joined, as above, but this time overlap the two, matching the threads and tacking together so that they cannot move. Now complete the embroidery, working through both layers. The width of the overlap will vary with the gauge of the canvas; it should not be wider than necessary, but wide enough to make a strong join.

Freely worked stitches in perlé and crewel yarns. The canvas was first coloured with fabric paint, applied with a printing block, to simulate a stone wall (Sample by Vicky Lugg)

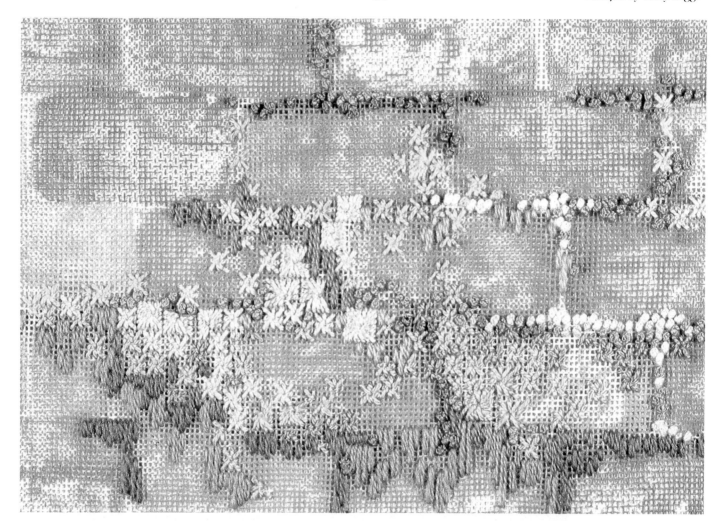

CHAPTER 4

STITCHES *for* CANVASWORK

N.B. Left-handed needlewomen may find it helpful to work from the stitch diagrams reflected in a mirror so that they are reversed.

There are dozens of stitches for canvaswork. A selection is included here and many more will be found in any good stitch book. All canvas stitches are formed with vertical, horizontal or diagonal straight stitches counted over the threads of the canvas; the number of threads covered regulates the size of the stitch. It is important to remember to count the threads, *not* the holes, otherwise some stitches will not work out properly. When stitching canvas in

the traditional manner, or when working something functional which is likely to receive wear and tear, there are three rules to bear in mind:

1 The stitches should completely cover the canvas.

2 Stitches should all be worked in the same way and all top stitches (e.g. in cross stitch or double cross stitch) should lie in the same direction.

3 As far as possible maintain an even tension and rhythm when stitching. This becomes easier with practice.

18. Sampler of canvaswork stitches by Adrienne Walker. Note how contrasting scale has been used with some stitches and also the variety of threads which changes the appearance of some stitches

However, the rules can be stretched when working panels for decorative purposes or making experiments.

A number of canvaswork stitches can be worked in two or more colours, in more than one thickness of thread, or even with different threads, e.g. one shiny and one matt thread. A good example of this is rice stitch, which offers much scope for ringing the changes. By using two or more threads of different colours in the same needle – say one terracotta thread plus one green thread plus one grey thread, or two dark blue threads with one pale blue thread – subtle mixes of colour can be achieved. This method is very effective when working buildings, brick walls, roofs, etc. It can also serve to make an expanse of background more interesting. Random lengths of thread in several tones of one colour used in sequence can also give variety to a background. Many variations on these themes can be devised.

Many canvasworkers today are using stitches which were formerly regarded as belonging exclusively to other embroidery techniques, e.g. raised chain band, herringbone stitch and couching – often very effectively. (Mary Rhodes has done much to pioneer in this area, using surface stitches to create exciting and unexpected textures.)

It is no longer the rule that every stitch should be identical to the preceding stitch and the succeeding one. Changing the scale of stitches where appropriate adds interest. If you work to a count of, say, four threads, then the number can be halved or doubled as necessary. Otherwise you may be left with awkward areas to fill, or it may be necessary to fill in with another stitch such as tent stitch. Of course this can be done deliberately to give contrast.

In less conventional work stitches can be distorted, elongated or compressed, and an area of regular stitching can break up into freely worked stitches. However, there is little point in covering an area of canvas with free stitchery which could just as well be worked on a non-canvas surface, unless the free stitchery forms an integral part of the design. Try experimenting with stitches – less familiar ones as well as the popular ones – working samples which can be kept for future reference. Change the scale of the canvas and the threads to see what happens; take one

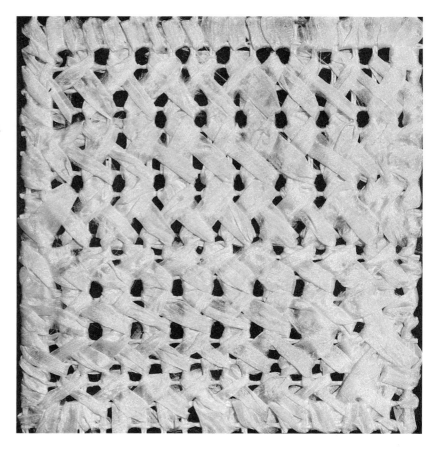

stitch and work it in several different threads, both thick and thin. Make other experiments – the more you do, the more ideas will come.

Stitches are the embroiderer's vocabulary. Many can be used to make patterns, and nearly all will give contrasting areas of texture. Changing the direction of stitches, when using one colour of thread only, introduces subtle changes of tone.

Always select stitches with a view to their purpose. For instance, if raised stitches such as double cross (Smyrna) stitch are subjected to friction, as on a chair seat, they will get dirty quickly and the top thread may wear through in a comparatively short time. This is very disappointing when many hours have been spent on a piece of work.

Tent stitch and **cross stitch** are probably the best-known canvaswork stitches. Tent stitch is extremely hard-wearing, as can be seen from the hangings and upholstered furniture which have survived the centuries. It is best worked on a frame, as it has a tendency

19. Sample, 150 cm (6 in) square. Rug canvas covered with herringbone stitch using torn strips of thin silk fabric. (Elizabeth Ashurst)

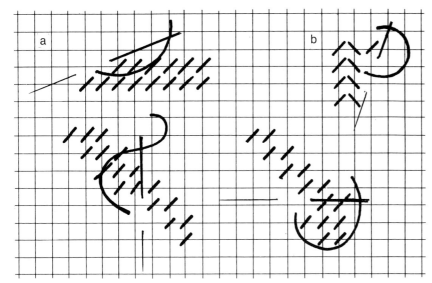

20. (a) Tent stitch: a small stitch which is useful for filling odd shapes, and is also very hard-wearing. Because it has a diagonal 'pull', it should be worked as shown to avoid distorting the canvas and, for the same reason, should be worked on a frame. The diagonal method of working is particularly suitable for larger areas as it gives a very even surface.
(b) Reverse tent stitch has a slightly patterned look as the light catches the stitches in different ways. For maximum effect use a thread with a sheen, such as perlé

to pull the canvas out of shape. To counteract this it should be worked as shown in figure 20, so that it makes a short diagonal stitch on the surface and a longer diagonal stitch at the back of the work; the canvas is then completely covered, making a dense, hard-wearing fabric. When working a large area of tent stitch – filling in the background on a cushion or panel, for example – the alternative, diagonal method of working is advisable as it gives a more even finish. Tent stitch can be combined with other stitches and is useful for filling in odd spaces, awkward shapes or very small areas. **Reverse tent stitch** can be worked vertically or horizontally.

Cross stitch should be worked by completing one stitch at a time. It is tempting to work **half cross stitch** right across an area and then work back to complete the crosses, but this is not so satisfactory. The golden rule for cross stitch is to make sure that all the top stitches cross in the same direction, otherwise the surface will look uneven. There may be times, of course, when this is the required effect! **Half cross** is sometimes worked over a laid thread on double thread canvas, making a dense background. This is referred to as 'tramming'.

There are a number of variations on cross stitch. **Straight cross stitch**, sometimes referred to as **upright cross**, is usually worked over two threads of the canvas, with the rows slotting into each other. Work each stitch separately, and follow the rule for cross

stitches – the top 'stroke' (in this case the horizontal stitch) must be the same in each stitch. An area of straight cross makes a very pleasing texture. Cross stitch and straight cross can be combined to form other stitches and surface patterns.

Long-armed or long-legged cross stitch covers the ground quite quickly, and can be worked vertically or horizontally. The traditional Portuguese Arraiolos (needlework rugs) also use this stitch diagonally. It is a good stitch for outlining borders. When worked in parallel rows close together it has a corded appearance.

Oblong cross stitch tends to leave canvas showing between the rows, but this can be overcome by working lines of back stitch between them. Back stitch can also be used to tie down each stitch at the centre, either with the same colour thread or with a contrast. Unlike the basic cross stitch it is worked in two journeys.

Reversed cross stitch uses diagonal and straight cross stitches worked in chequerboard fashion and then crossed with a finer thread. There is scope for experiment here.

Double (Smyrna) cross stitch makes a nice texture, as the surface is slightly raised. A straight cross is worked on top of a diagonal cross and, once again, the top stitches must all lie in the same direction. Complete one stitch at a time. Double cross can also be outlined with back stitch.

21. **Cross stitches**

(a) Cross stitch: note that the top stitch of every cross should point in the same direction; cross stitches should be completed one at a time

(b) Half cross stitch can be worked on single or double canvas

(c) Straight cross stitch makes a good texture when worked solidly, rather like moss stitch in knitting. It can also be alternated with larger diagonal crosses to make a patterned surface

(d) Long-armed (or long-legged) cross stitch covers the ground quickly. When worked in close rows it has a corded appearance

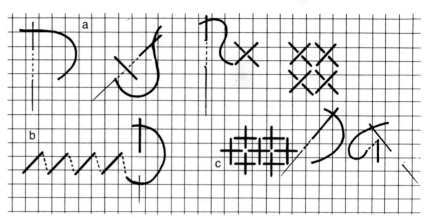

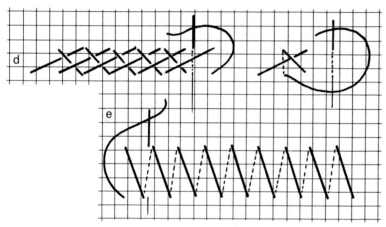

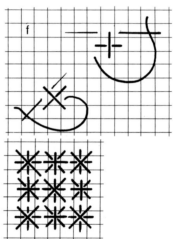

(e) Oblong cross stitch is a variation of cross stitch; the centre of the stitch can be tied down with back stitch in contrasting or self-coloured thread. If the canvas shows, a line of back stitch can also be worked between rows

(f) Reversed cross stitch: straight and diagonal cross stitches are worked alternately; every stitch is then crossed with its opposite, i.e. diagonal cross over straight cross, and vice versa. Experiments can be made with different colours and thicknesses of thread

(g) Double cross stitch consists of a straight cross on top of a diagonal cross. The top stitch should always be worked in the same direction

(h) Rice stitch is a most attractive stitch. By changing the threads and colours of the crosses and crossed corners, subtle colour changes can be made and formal or freer patterns created. The ground is covered with cross stitches; the corners of the crosses are then crossed with another stitch. Where there is a large area of rice stitch this can be done by working along the rows, but for areas of two or three stitches the stitches can be completed one at a time if it is more convenient

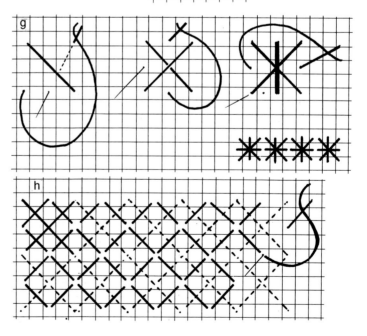

Small 'garden' panel worked entirely in stranded cotton in tent and velvet stitches, by Joanne Satchell (Embroiderers' Guild Collection)

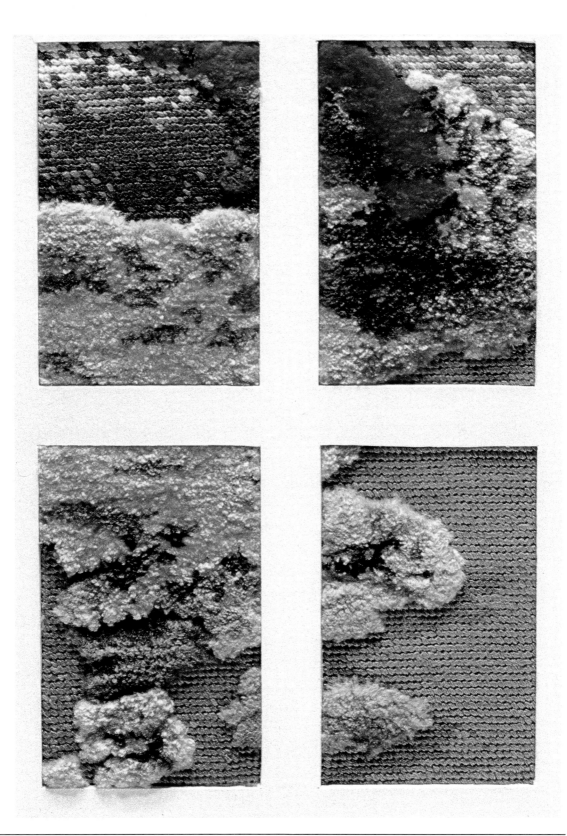

Rice Stitch is a particularly attractive stitch based on cross stitch. The crossed corners can be worked in different colours, different threads, or different thicknesses of thread, to give an interesting variety of texture and tones. By changing the colours of both crosses and corners, either in random fashion or in a more orderly progression, subtle colour changes will emerge.

Straight or satin stitches worked vertically, horizontally or diagonally, make the most use of the play of light on the surface. By changing the direction of the stitch while working in one colour, changes of tone will appear, particularly so if the thread used is a slightly shiny one, such as perlé (pearl) cotton. The family of straight stitches includes **flat stitch**, which is many people's favourite stitch. When worked in one colour it makes full use of stitch direction, and it also makes an attractive patterned surface, both in one colour and if more than one colour is used. It covers the ground very quickly.

Byzantine Stitch is also a useful stitch for backgrounds. It may need careful counting at first, but becomes easier with practice. A random-dyed thread could produce interesting results, as could changing the direction of the stitch on alternate bands. It shades well if several tones of one colour are used in succeeding rows.

Brick stitch can be worked horizontally or vertically and is much used for buildings – bricks and roof tiles. Worked with two or three different colours in the needle, it can be very effective.

Parisian stitch is a small filling stitch worked over one and three threads alternately. **Hungarian stitch** is akin to Parisian stitch, but is worked over two and four threads. Two or more tones of one colour can be introduced, or it can be worked in contrasting colours, when the reason for its alternative name, 'mosaic stitch' becomes apparent.

Florentine stitch, which belongs to this group, is dealt with separately in the chapter 'Patterns in Canvaswork'.

There are several variations on the basic **straight gobelin stitch**. These include **slanting gobelin**, which is a larger version of tent stitch, being worked over one thread across and two threads in depth; and also **encroaching gobelin** and **plaited gobelin**.

22. Variations on rice stitch. Here the stitch is worked over various numbers of threads to give different scale; a wide variety of yarns was also used. Note also the variety of patterns made with this one stitch (Vicky Lugg)

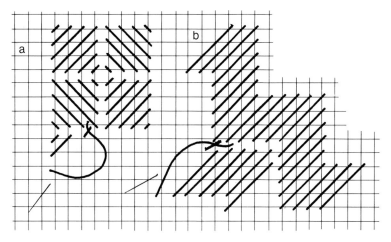

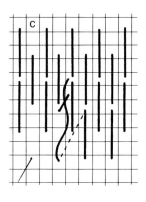

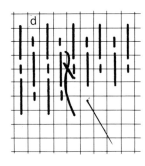

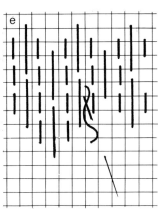

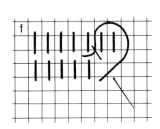

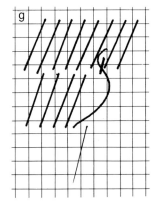

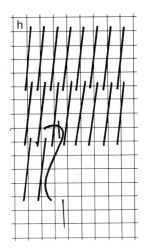

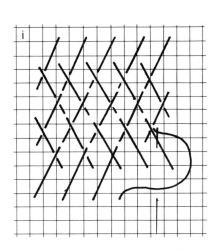

23a. Straight or satin stitches

(a) Flat stitch is sometimes referred to as 'mosaic stitch'. It covers the ground quickly and can be worked in one colour and completed in another, or it can be worked in stripes of different colours. Many other variations can be introduced

(b) Byzantine stitch: a good stitch for covering areas of background. It can be shaded in the manner of Florentine stitch

(c) Brick stitch: a good background stitch which can be worked vertically or horizontally. It is popular for architectural subjects, when it is used to indicate bricks

(d) Parisian stitch can be worked over 1 and 3 threads or over 2 and 4 threads, making a close filling. One colour can be used throughout, or contrasting colours can be used for succeeding rows; tones of one colour might also be tried

(e) Hungarian stitch, like Parisian stitch, is worked in rows of one colour, contrasting colours, or different tones of one colour

(f) Straight gobelin stitch is similar to satin stitch. If there is a tendency for the canvas to show, it can be worked over a long padding stitch laid across the canvas between the threads

(g) Slanting gobelin stitch is shown here worked over 4 horizontal and 2 vertical threads.

(h) Encroaching gobelin stitch covers the canvas well. Note that the rows of stitches interlock

(i) Plaited gobelin stitch: this looks more complicated than it is. Each succeeding row crosses the row before.

23b. Straight stitch worked directionally to make the most of the play of light. Only one colour of perlé was used throughout but it looks as though more than one colour has been introduced. The effect is enhanced by using a thread which has a sheen (Margaret Rivers)

Other useful canvaswork stitches include **chain stitch**, which looks like the right side of knitted stocking stitch and makes a smooth surface. If worked over more than one thread the canvas may show through. If this is unacceptable fill in with back stitch. (There is also a knitting stitch worked rather differently in two journeys on double thread canvas.)
Fern stitch is worked in rows; the width and depth of the stitch can be varied. **Fishbone stitch** makes an attractive chevron pattern. **Ray stitch** is a good filling stitch with a pleasing pattern. Experiments with the proportions of the stitch could give some interesting results. **Web stitch** covers the canvas densely with a fine, even texture.

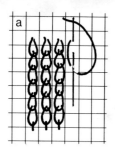
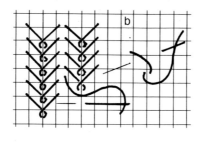
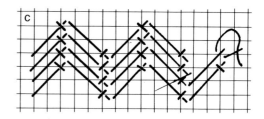

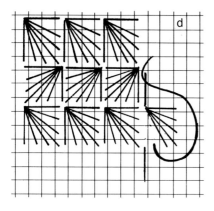
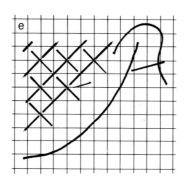

24. *Other useful stitches*
(a) Chain stitch on canvas looks very like a knitted stitch when it is completed. It is worked in the same way as surface chain stitch, but uses the threads of the canvas as a support. A line of back stitch can be added over the stitches if the canvas shows through
(b) Fern stitch: each row is worked from the top downwards. The stitch can be worked solidly or, in more experimental work, it can be spaced out or the width changed
(c) Fishbone stitch is traditionally worked in close rows, but experiments could be tried with the width and angle of the stitches. This stitch could also be worked in blocks of colour
(d) Ray stitch makes an attractive filling
(e) Web stitch has a woven look. Each row is completed before starting the next

Ribbons applied to canvas with simple stitches,
interspersed with bands of stitchery. The threads are
various weights of perlé to contrast with the velvet
ribbons (Vicky Lugg)

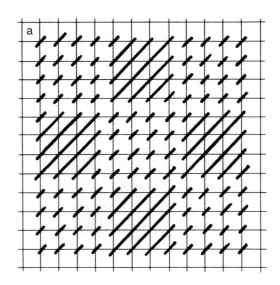

COMPOSITE STITCHES

Two stitches sometimes combine to make other stitches. **Chequer stitch** consists of squares of tent stitch and diagonal satin stitch, alternating to give a chequerboard appearance. Contrasting colours in different combinations could be used to give a variety of patterns. **Scottish stitch** is rather similar to chequer stitch, blocks of diagonal satin stitch being divided from each other by rows of tent stitch. Colour variations could be tried, the rows of tent stitch increased, or the direction of the satin stitch blocks changed.

   Jacquard stitch is good for backgrounds. It is similar to Byzantine stitch, but the rows are divided by a line of tent stitch – usually one row, but more could be added.

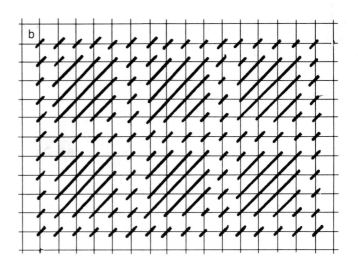

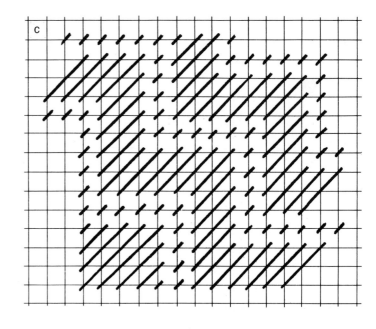

*25. **Composite stitches***
(a) Chequer stitch: tent and satin stitches are worked in alternate blocks and the stitches all lie in the same direction
(b) Scottish stitch: worked in tent and satin stitches, this stitch relies for its effect on the contrasting textures
(c) Jacquard stitch is very similar to Byzantine stitch, but has a row of tent stitch worked between the rows of satin stitch

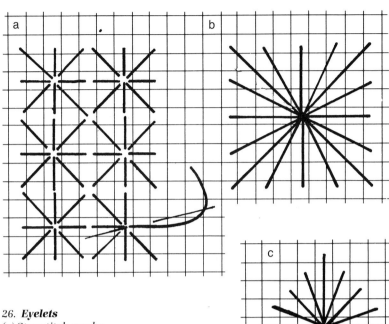

26. Eyelets
(a) Star stitch can be worked singly or in an all-over pattern
(b) Eye stitch can be framed with a line of back stitch if wished
(c) Diamond eyelets can also be framed with a line of back stitch

27. Raised stitches: (a) Rhodes stitch (b) Velvet stitch

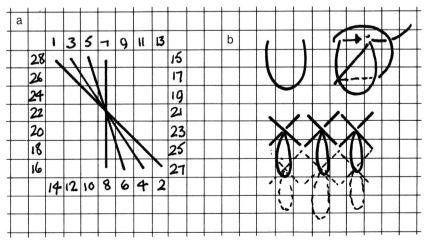

EYELETS

Eyelets and similar stitches can be used singly, or be closely worked to cover the ground completely. **Star stitch** makes a nice all-over ground but does not completely cover the canvas. It should not be confused with **Algerian eye stitch**, in which two stitches instead of one are taken into the centre each time and pulled tightly; it is also worked diagonally and not in rows as shown here.

Eye stitch is usually finished with a surround of back stitches, though this is not essential. It makes an attractive border. **Diamond eyelets** are a close relation of eye stitch. The eyelets can be finished with a row of back stitch if wished.

RAISED STITCHES

Raised stitches add interest and make a good contrast to areas of flat stitchery. They should not be used, however, where they may get rubbed, as the top threads will wear out quickly.

Rhodes stitch is a very popular stitch which can be worked in almost any size and also to shapes other than a square. It combines well with areas of flat stitch or tent stitch.

Rows of **velvet stitch** should be worked from the bottom up. The loops can be left uncut or cut to make a raised pile. Soft or fluffy yard will give the best results if the loops are to be cut. The stitch is very similar to the 'plush stitch' used in Berlin woolwork. A gauge can be used to obtain an even pile.

SUPERIMPOSING

A solid background of tent stitch, or stitches giving a fairly flat surface, can be further embellished with couching or other surface stitches such as fly, buttonhole, chain, etc., or knots.

CHAPTER 5

PATTERNS *in* CANVASWORK

Chambers' Dictionary tells us that pattern is 'a decorative design; a particular disposition of form and colours; a design or figure repeated indefinitely'. Patterns enrich a surface, and the even weave of canvas immediately suggests the formal and geometrical patterns to which canvaswork stitches lend themselves. Some canvaswork stitches are patterns in themselves, e.g. flat, Scottish and chequer stitches.

Many happy hours can be spent 'doodling' with felt-tip pens or crayons, creating patterns on graph paper – each square on the paper representing a stitch or group of stitches – or with needle and thread on a spare piece of canvas. Keep all these doodles and small samples for future inspiration.

Patterns are all around us – on glass, pottery and china; in the weave of textiles and basketwork; a line of books on a shelf may suggest a pattern, or a pile of bricks in a builder's yard; a heap of striped deckchairs at the seaside can spark off an idea. Ethnic artefacts are rich in patterns, as are tiles and buildings – the choice is endless, and all that is needed is a 'seeing eye'.

Old needlework books sometimes contain cross stitch patterns which can be adapted to canvaswork. Museums are a wonderful source of ideas for patterns, and an hour or two spent wandering around and making notes is time well spent. Always carry a small notebook or sketchbook and a pencil, ready to note down anything that appeals. The camera is also an extremely useful recording instrument. All these notes, together with postcards, photographs, rough sketches and other relevant material, can be kept in a file ready for reference when needed.

All-over patterns are built up on a grid system. The proportions of the grid can be changed and patterns can contract or expand. Parts of the grid can move directionally, making brick or half-drop patterns. Sections of the grid can be further divided.

Motifs can be repeated or combined with other motifs. Band or border patterns can be devised from the same motifs. Motifs can be made to turn a corner (a mirror is helpful with this). A motif can be added to, or things can be taken away. Units can be made larger or smaller, or they can be turned round.

Designs made up of triangles can be planned successfully on isometric graph paper, obtainable from good stationers and graphic art suppliers. They can then be translated on to canvas using triangular blocks of satin stitches. By working with triangles it is possible to make a pattern of hexagons.

Colour can play an important part in pattern. The same pattern worked in different colour schemes changes its character completely. An area of pattern worked throughout in the same colours could be dull; try introducing an unexpected touch of colour to make it much more exciting.

28. *Experimenting with patterns by working directly on to the canvas. This makes a useful piece of reference material (Margaret Rivers)*

Texture is important too. A pattern of stitches worked in one colour only can still be made interesting by using contrasting texture – rough against smooth, or a shiny thread contrasted with a matt thread. There are many possibilities.

The making of patterns is fascinating. Experiment, let one thing lead to another, and pleasant surprises will result.

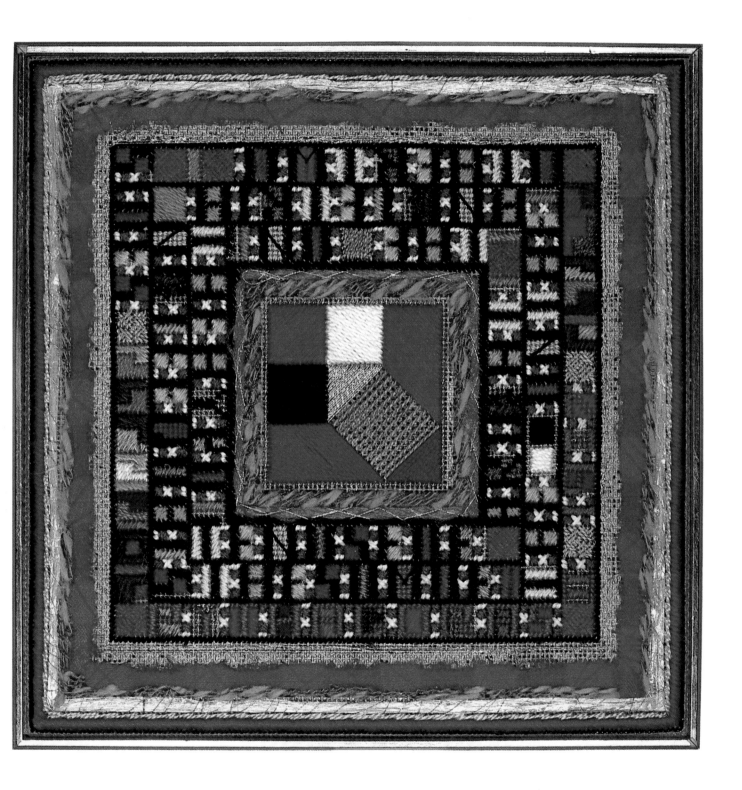

'Pythagoras II'. Canvaswork panel by Jenifer Murray

29. *'Four styles', a small panel. The flowers are impressionistic, the vase has minimal stitching, there is traditional stitching at the bottom of the panel and the main background behind the flowers is painted and overstitched to give the appearance of tiles or wallpaper. Worked for fun as an experiment (Jenifer Murray)*

30. *(Below) Some sources of inspiration for patterns: (Left) a postcard of a painting by Sonia Delaunay; (Centre top) a Maori woodcarving; (Centre bottom) broken snow fences, beside the railway through the Drumochter Pass in Scotland; (Right top) a border from an ancient Greek pot; (Right bottom) a duck from a Persian tile, a piece of ancient jewellery and a fragment of a wall painting*

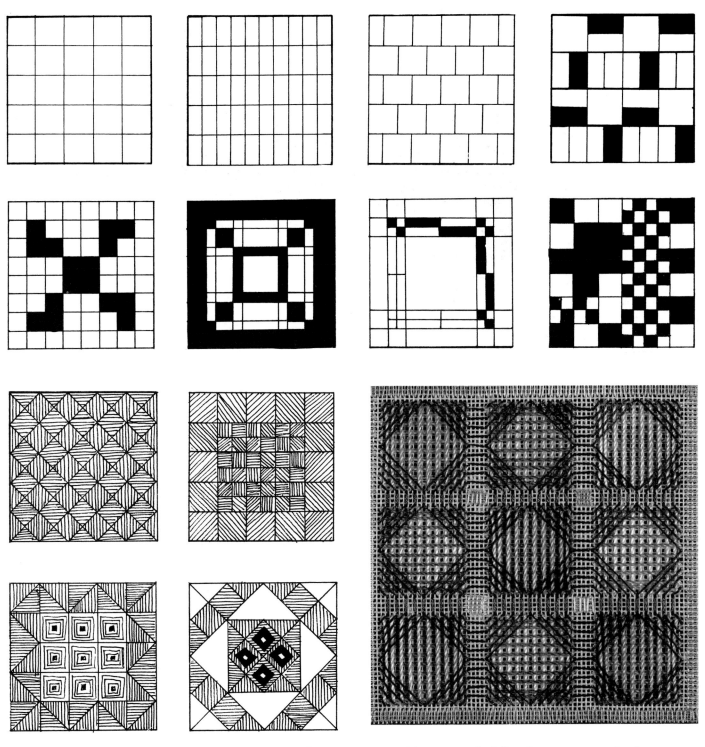

31. Using a grid to build up patterns. The pattern units can be repeated to make borders or all-over patterns

32. A grid pattern worked directly on to canvas using three layers of long stitches. The canvas was backed with a dark-coloured silk which helped to show up the grid of the canvas itself (Margaret Rivers)

33. *Mathematical progressions can be used to space strips or bands both vertically and/or horizontally. This is a fascinating exercise. A dark grid imposed on top of a background of brilliant colour can be dramatic*

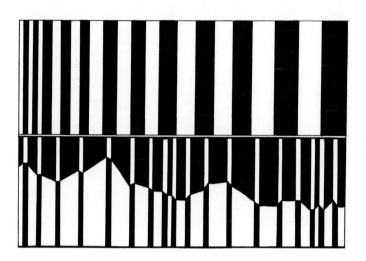
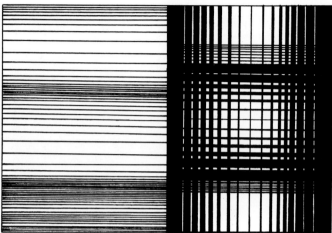

34. *Isometric graph paper used to build up patterns based on the equilateral triangle*

Sampler worked in tapestry wool showing the breakdown of stitches into complementary colours (Vicky Lugg)

35. Partly-worked panel by Jenifer Murray. Some of the background is painted in preparation for free stitchery. Framed by a border of patterns taken from many sources

Florentine patterns

Florentine patterns (also known as Bargello, flame stitch and Hungarian point) enjoy a deserved popularity. Once the 'base line' has been established they are quick and easy to work, attractive to look at, lend themselves to many different settings and uses, and the variations on the pattern itself are infinite. Florentine is also very soothing to work!

The characteristics of Florentine work are the curving patterns and the careful grading through tones of one colour, from dark to light or *vice versa*. This can give an almost three-dimensional effect when well done. Occasionally the progression of tones is interrupted by the introduction of a contrasting colour, or the arrangement of tones is changed.

There are a number of surviving examples of Florentine work, some dating back to the seventeenth century. No doubt because of its speed of working, it was popular for bed hangings and covering upholstered furniture, but it also crops up quite frequently on smaller items. There is more than one story quoted concerning its origins, the most popular being that which claims that the work was introduced to Italy by the Hungarian bride of one of the Florentine Medici family.

The Florentine stitch is similar to satin stitch. A single thread canvas is necessary and it will be seen from the diagrams that the stitch can be worked in different ways to suit the embroiderer's convenience. Wool, silk or cotton thread is suitable, as long as it is thick enough to cover the canvas adequately without being lumpy. In some cases it is better to use a finer canvas rather than increase the number of strands in the needle, which can look clumsy. A natural-coloured canvas is less obtrusive than white, which has a tendency to 'flicker' between the stitches. It is important in Florentine work not to use too long a thread; if the thread is worn in by continually passing through the canvas it will make thin patches, which show up badly and look most unsightly. Aim for an even tension and a smooth surface. Florentine is the one form of canvaswork which can be worked successfully in the hand if wished, as there is no diagonal pull on the stitches. However, the finished work will still be improved by the use of a frame.

The curving patterns look more complicated than they really are. They are built up with blocks of straight stitches, the depth and width of each being changed to make the required curve. These curves can be worked out on graph paper or directly on to canvas.

To start working a Florentine pattern, mark the exact centre of the canvas with tacking stitches as shown.

Begin at the centre of the canvas with the centre stitch of one repeat of the pattern, and work out sideways in both directions until the required width is reached. *This is the 'base line'*. Every successive line is identical except for the change of tone/colour. Continue the gradation of tone/colour upwards and

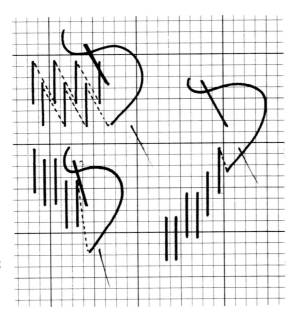

36a. Alternative methods of working Florentine stitch

36b. Method of working out Florentine curves and patterns on graph paper

downwards until the work is completed. If several tones of one colour are being used, it may be helpful to number the skeins of yarn in rotation. A mistake may entail a lot of unpicking if not seen immediately, which is very disheartening.

There are also more angular versions of Florentine work. These patterns too can be worked out on graph paper or directly on the canvas. Although different in character to the curving patterns they are equally attractive. Angular or curved patterns can be reversed to make other patterns.

Four-sided Florentine patterns give yet another dimension. They are particularly useful for filling square shapes, such as cushions and the tops of boxes. The pattern can be worked either from the outside inwards, or from the centre outwards.

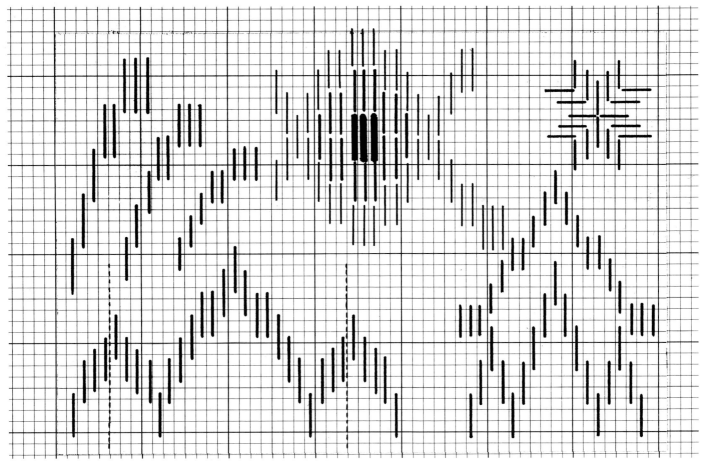

*Four-way Florentine (or Bargello) pattern worked in
a variety of threads (Vicky Lugg)*

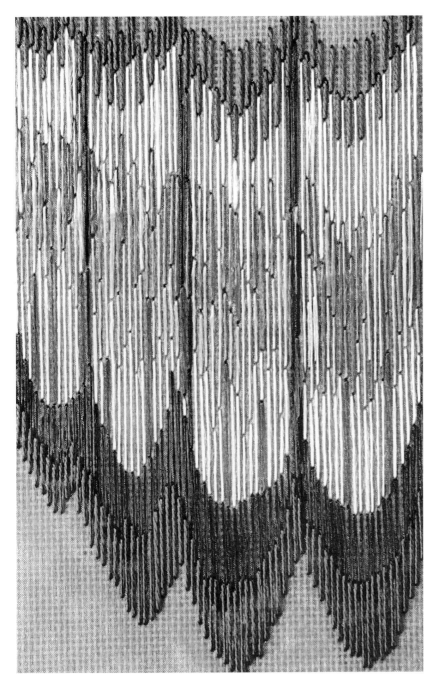

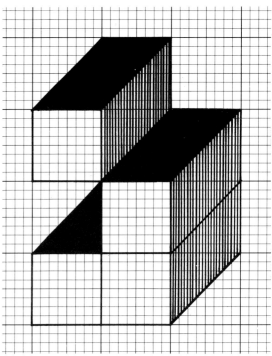

38. Three tones of colour arranged to simulate three dimensions

37. Design developed from studies of patterns on a shell. The canvas is behind a layer of gauze and the stitches, worked in several different threads, including perlé and silk floss, have been taken through both layers (Jaqui Bower)

'Free' Florentine breaks away from the regular patterns and makes a good all-over background. Small areas can be used as a contrast to other patterns and stitches and, if drawn out on graph paper, the drawing can be cut up and re-assembled to suggest further patterns.

Simulated three-dimensional patterns

These are made by using three or more colours, or tones of one colour (tone being the lightness or darkness of a colour), in a regular sequence. A pattern of this kind very familiar to many embroiderers is the 'Tumbling Blocks' pattern beloved of patchworkers, where a hexagon is divided into three equal diamonds; one is worked in a light colour, one in a medium colour and one in a dark colour, e.g. light, medium and dark blue, or white, grey and black. The pattern is used as a repeating unit. Changing the position of the tones gives different effects.

The same principle can be applied to other patterns so that they appear to come forward or to recede. Try doodling on graph paper or isometric graph paper with coloured crayons to find out what works (and what does not). Pads of patterned pages, designed for children to colour, are fun to experiment with, and can produce a wealth of pattern ideas. It is worth keeping an eye open in big stationers and bookshops for these and similar publications.

Interlaced patterns are an extension of the three-dimensional patterns; by using different colours or different tones of a colour, an appearance of interlacing can be achieved.

Berlin woolwork samplers in museums are a rich source of three-dimensional and interlaced patterns, as well as many others. Books on Celtic ornament are also a good source of reference.

39. (Left) Panel by Margaret Pascoe using three tones of thread to suggest three dimensions

40. (Right) Long stitches and various tones of soft embroidery thread suggest different levels. Some portions of the sample have actually been raised over painted cocktail sticks. The background canvas has also been dyed with coloured ink (Margaret Rivers)

41. (Below) Interlaced patterns can be worked out on graph paper. Here the same pattern has been treated in various ways, giving quite different appearances

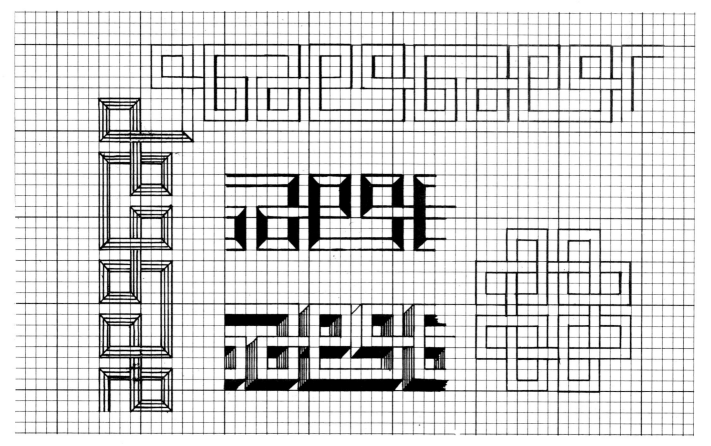

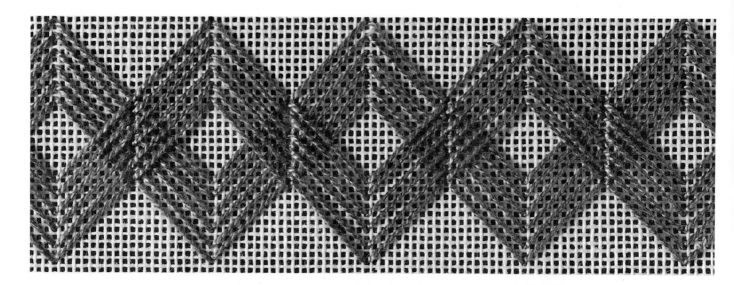

42. (Above) Long stitches used to make a 'three-dimensional' border (Margaret Rivers)

43. Pattern from a Berlin woolwork sampler. British, nineteenth century (Embroiderers' Guild Collection)

CHAPTER 6

DESIGNING *for* CANVASWORK

Many proficient embroiders were first introduced to embroidery in general, and canvaswork in particular, through a 'kit'. Kits have improved enormously over the last few years and can provide a good starting point, as well as a therapeutic occupation for those who have no desire to branch out on their own. However, designing an original piece of work is extremely satisfying and gives a sense of achievement.

What makes a good design? Most important it must take into account the limitations of the technique and materials the embroiderer intends to use. In the case of canvaswork, the canvas is a rigid, even-weave structure and its regular nature will give a stylized geometrical character to any image placed upon it. Balance and harmony in a design will make it pleasing to the eye. It will look 'right'.

Design means planning and choosing and, very often, discarding. It has already been noted that no amount of beautiful stitchery will conceal a poor design. This may sound daunting, but commonsense and a step-by-step approach will help to make it less so.

'Herbaceous Border'. Design sheet by Vicky Lugg. (Left) Small panel worked in various lengths of upright gobelin stitch using a thick, slightly twisted, rayon thread. (Right) Similar design translated into machine satin (zigzag) stitching on a fine canvas

Perhaps the best advice is to 'keep it simple' at first, and let experience be the guide. Train the eye by looking at paintings and examples of the other decorative arts, and noting composition, texture, colour and contrast.

Art materials

Designing is hard work, but it helps to have the right materials to hand. Although a lot can be done with a biro and the back of an old envelope, using the right tools is a pleasurable experience in itself and certainly gives better results.

There is a wide variety of materials on the market today and this can be confusing for the uninitiated. Take any opportunity you can to experiment with art materials, to find out what will work for you. Don't be afraid to experiment, making marks, creating textures, working layers of paint and paper one on top of the other – this should be fun, not a chore.

There is no need to spend a lot of money at first. The following basic list is more than adequate to begin designing for canvaswork:

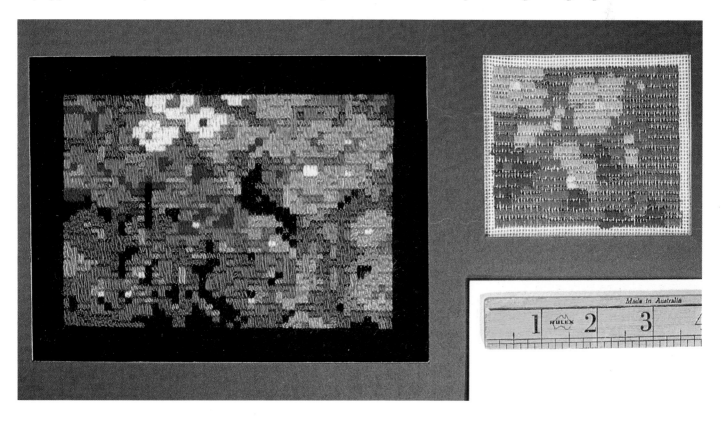

44. (Left) 'Commuters', a small panel by Gisela Banbury. Worked in tent stitch throughout it makes use of repeating units to create a light-hearted and very contemporary design

- Sketchbook/notebook for making notes and rough sketches as an *aide memoire*. Photographs, postcards, and developed designs can also be added.
- A selection of good quality pencils – H or harder for tracing, and HB, B, 2B, 3B or 4B for general use
- Knife or pencil sharpener
- Ruler
- Coloured felt-tip pens or crayons
- Tracing paper or greaseproof paper
- Graph paper; which comes in sheets or pads and in various size grids. Choose one which will be comfortable to work with – too fine and it could be a strain on the eyes
- Isometric graph paper is useful for working out designs in triangles, diamond or hexagon shapes.

Things like a compass, pastel crayons and paints can be added later.

Ways of arriving at a design

Satisfactory ideas for design do not spring from 'the top of the head' – not unless you have a very clear idea of what it is you want to do. Some embroiderers have the ability to translate their ideas directly into fabric and thread, but most need to think their ideas through from beginning to end and work out these ideas on paper. The finished work does not have to follow the design on paper slavishly; improvements and modifications may suggest themselves as the work progresses.

It is important when planning a piece of work to consider how it is to be presented when finished. Will it be framed? Perhaps the mount can be part of, or an extension of, the design? A little thought at this stage can avoid problems later.

First build up a bank of reference material to provide a source of inspiration. This can be culled from museums, holidays, days out in the country or in town, gardens, landscapes, natural objects, man-made objects, buildings, etc., and can include drawings, photographs, postcards, cuttings from magazines, catalogues and anything else relevant to particular topics which may interest you. Jot down notes of colour schemes and any other 'thoughts'. Most people lead busy lives and it is all too easy to forget such vital pieces of information. Keep all this material methodically in your sketchbook/notebook or in a box or file so that it is readily accessible.

Drawing skills are useful and can be acquired with perserverance and a positive attitude. Drawing for many embroiderers is a form of note-taking; it does not matter if the marks and squiggles only make sense to the embroiders, no one else need see them. Most importantly, drawing is also a means of increasing awareness and observation. The

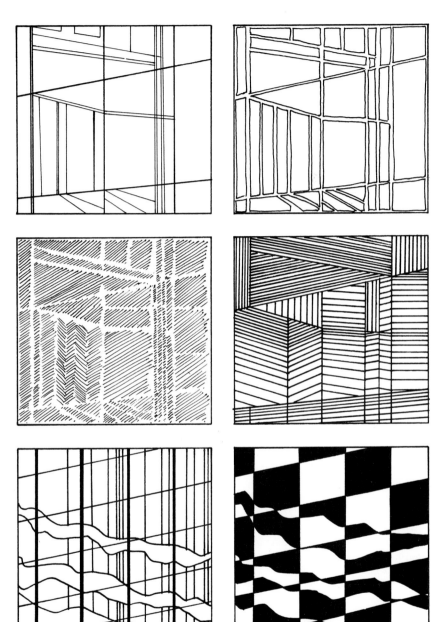

pencil is not the only medium; paint, pastels, crayons and felt-tip pens, among other things, can be used to jot down references and develop ideas. One idea soon leads to another and the more you do, the more ideas will come.

Line, shape, form, colour and texture

Lines can be used to express movement, to enclose shapes, to emphasize forms. A line can be continuous, or it can be broken at intervals and become a series of dashes. It can be thick or thin, straight or curved, spiky or sinuous, smooth or bumpy – or any combination of these. Horizontal, vertical and diagonal lines suggest different qualities.

The **shape** of something identifies it for us. Shapes can be repeated or superimposed. Contrasting shapes add variety. Negative shapes (the spaces in between shapes) are as important as the shapes themselves. Overlapping shapes gives more shapes.

Form is three-dimensional where shape is two-dimensional. On a flat surface form can be suggested by perspective or the use of tones.

Tone refers to lightness or darkness. In pigment white and black are added to pure colour in different proportions to create a variety of tones.

Colour makes an immediate impact. It is the first thing the eye sees. It can be used deliberately to create a mood or required effect, such as red for anger. Colour can also be used symbolically, but note that the same colour can mean different things in different parts of the world. For instance, in England white is used for weddings, but in India white signifies mourning.

The **primary colours** are *red*, *blue* and *yellow*. The **secondary colours** are made up by mixing primary colours:

Red + Blue	=	*Violet*
Blue + Yellow	=	*Green*
Yellow + Red	=	*Orange*

Vary the proportions of the mixtures and a whole range of colours can be made. Increase the red in violet and it will become reddish-violet; increase the blue in violet and it will

45. One idea can be interpreted in several different ways. Here the drawing at top left was based on a quick sketch of office windows. The idea was then taken further; the two at the bottom have changed character slightly by the introduction of 'clouds', and taking liberties with the verticals and diagonals. This can be described as 'doodling', and can give rise to many ideas. A small section of one of these doodles could be further developed into yet more designs

become blueish violet. Increase the blue in green and it will become blueish green; Increase the yellow in green and it will become yellowish-green. Increase the yellow in orange and it will become yellowish-orange; increase the red in orange and it will become reddish-orange.

Mix all three primary colours in varying proportions to obtain neutrals – greys and browns.

These theories apply to pigment, but can also be helpful when using fabrics and threads. For example, flat areas of colour can be broken up and made more interesting by a scattering of stitches in another colour. Try working a small area in, say, red; begin to add a few orange stitches, then more and more until the red is eliminated; continue to work in orange and then begin to add yellow until the orange is eliminated; now add red, and observe the colour changes. Colour exercises like this are fun to do and can be carried on into designs.

TERMS USED WHEN REFERRING TO COLOUR

Hue: the name of a colour, e.g. red
Saturated colour: pure colour
Intensity: the purity or dullness of a colour
Value: the lightness or darkness of a colour
Shade: a pure colour to which black has been added
Tint: a pure colour to which white has been added
Tone: a pure colour to which black *and* white have been added
Complementary colours: those which lie directly opposite each other on the colour wheel. They are the strongest contrasts, i.e. red/green, blue/orange, yellow/violet
Analogous colours: those which lie next to each other on the colour wheel, e.g. red, reddish-violet, violet

Proportion of colour is important. An equal quantity of two colours can result in a dull piece of work, which looks uninteresting. Change the proportions and it becomes much more lively.

A small amount of very bright colour enlivens an overall scheme of dull colours; it could also make a focal point. A small amount of dull colour combined with very bright colours can be dramatic. The same design

looks very different if the colours are transposed or the colour scheme is changed entirely.

Colours change if placed on different background colours. A red on a pink background will appear to be a different red if placed on a green background, for example.

On the colour wheel, colours adjacent to red and orange give a feeling of warmth and are referred to as 'warm' colours; colours in the blue area are regarded as 'cool' colours. A green which contains more yellow than blue is a 'warm' green; a green which contains more blue than yellow is a 'cool' green. Warm colours appear to come forward; cool colours appear to recede. This illusion can be exploited in a design. In a landscape, for example, cool colours used in the distance and warm colours used in the foreground give a feeling of depth. Similarly, pale colours in the distance and strong colours in the foreground will suggest distance.

When working large areas of canvas try using two threads of contrasting colour in the needle, or two tones of the same colour. Change one of the threads at intervals while working and subtle colour changes will result. There are many variations on this theme waiting to be discovered.

Colour is a very personal thing and these are only intended as basic notes. To increase awareness of colour and its possibilities, observe colour in nature and colour in art; make notes of colour schemes and other points you want to remember. For example, take a pebble or a dying leaf, or a reproduction of a painting, and study it carefully. How many colours can you see in it? Try making an analysis on paper of these colours using paint or crayons; observe the proportion of one colour to another. Match the colours as nearly as possible with scraps of fabric or thread wrapped round a strip of card. Sections of the completed exercises may provide interesting colour combinations.

With coloured papers, paint or crayons make some experiments with primary and secondary colours, also complementary and analogous colours. Then substitute shades and tints for the pure colours. These colour 'notes' can be useful when planning a piece of work.

(Right) Sample showing gradated colour change (Ann Rutherford)

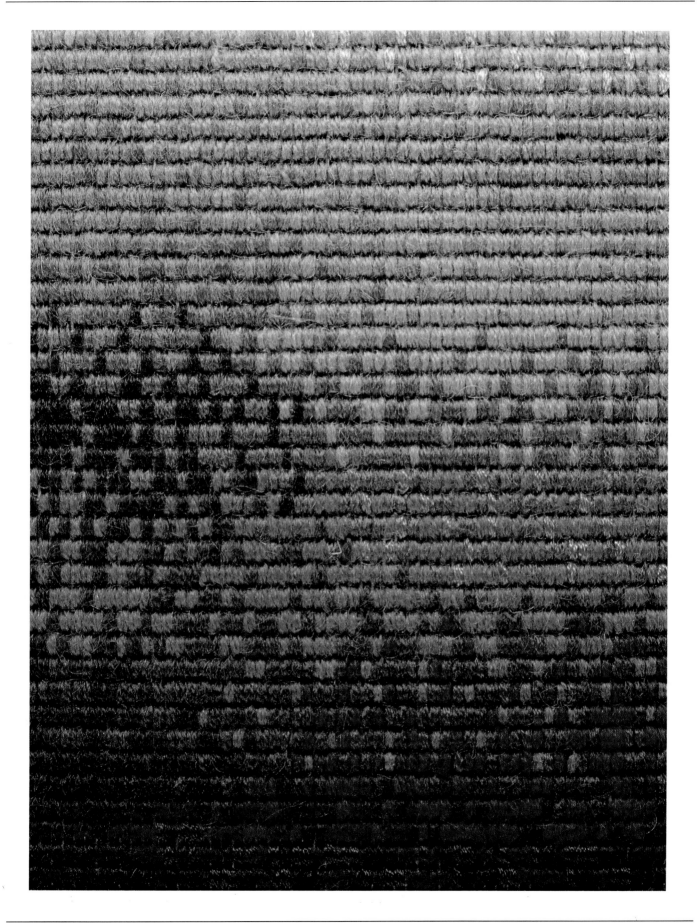

Texture is another important element in embroidery. As with colour, observe and record textures for future reference. Photocopying is a good way of recording textures in textiles, and rubbings of bark, wood and other surfaces provide a wealth of contrasting textures; use a soft pencil or conté crayon with thin paper to do this.

Lettering

It is sometimes necessary to use lettering to convey information in the form of monograms, names and messages. (Lettering on old samplers served two purposes: the child learnt her stitches and her alphabet at the same time.) Many old needlework magazines and books carry illustrations of monograms and alphabets. Some are very ornamental, being decorated with flower sprays or curlicues.

For modern alphabets, a book of typefaces or the catalogues of rub-down lettering suppliers are a useful source of inspiration. Some of the more inventive designer alphabets are easily adapted to canvaswork. When using lettering, space the letters of each word closely together. Words also should be spaced fairly closely. If spaced too far apart the eye tends to jump from one to the next, rather than reading the word or sentence as a whole. If letters are to convey any sort of message they must be legible. This is not usually a problem in canvaswork but it is worth bearing in mind.

By changing colours or stitch direction some modern alphabets take on an almost abstract quality, and can be used as repeating band patterns, or adapted to form units for all-over patterns, perhaps by changing the spacing or scale of the units.

Letters can also be used as a starting point for design. One or more letters can be traced, tracings superimposed on one another, further tracings taken, then cut up and re-assembled. Lettering of all shapes and sizes from which tracings can be taken will be found in newspaper and magazine advertisements, posters, etc. Alternatively, letters can be cut out free-hand in stiff paper and used as a starting point.

Designing for three-dimensional items

Three-dimensional items pose special problems. The component parts of a design – the front and back of a bag, say – need to relate to one another so that they form a pleasing whole, and practical considerations such as wear and tear also need to be taken into account. When designing, remember that some three-dimensional objects will be seen from several different angles.

The same design can be contracted or expanded to fill different shapes; the same

46. 'The Exuberant Garden', panel 11.5 cm (4^1/$_2$ in) × 9 cm (3^1/$_2$ in). Painted canvas worked with a variety of threads mostly silk and stitches to make an interesting texture. Wrapped plastic drinking straws were used to raise the centre of the panel (Christine Cooper)

47. (Above) Victorian fancywork: punched paper
worked with cross stitches (Embroiderers' Guild
Collection)

48. (Below) 'Astra', a modern typeface, adapted to
canvaswork by planning it on graph paper. Letters
from the alphabet have been used to make the
monogram 'MR', the letter 'Y' has been spaced out
and could well be used as a pattern unit, and the
letter 'F' has been cut up and re-arranged. Many
effects could be achieved by colouring in different
parts of these designs

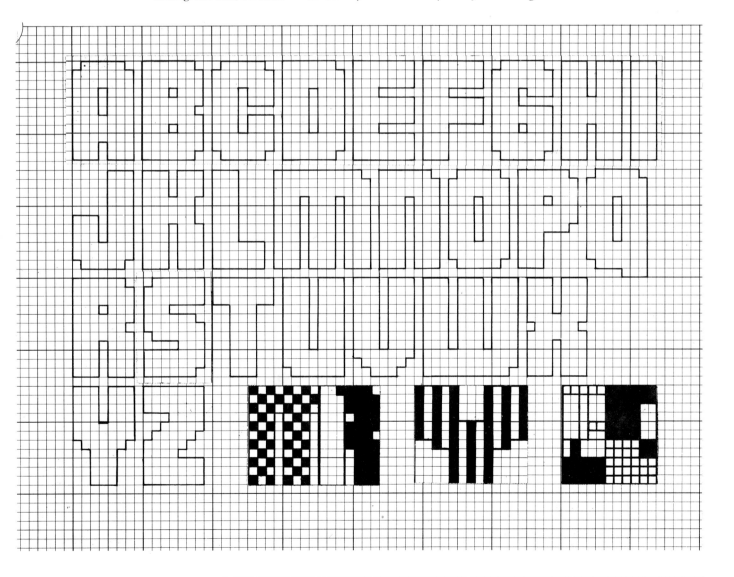

border can be used to contain different motifs; in some cases (e.g. a box or a cushion) the design can continue right round the object so that it 'encloses' it without an obvious join. This needs careful planning and measuring, especially if the embroidery is being worked in sections and assembled at a later stage.

Try to avoid any suggestion that the decoration is an after-thought. It should be an integral part of the whole.

Enlarging and reducing designs

To enlarge a design, first take a tracing of it. Over the tracing draw a grid of 6mm ($^1/_4$ in) squares. Now prepare another grid to the required overall size and divide it up into the same number of squares. Number the corresponding squares on both grids and then, using the squares on the grids as a guide, copy the original tracing. Many people will be familiar with this procedure from children's drawing books.

To reduce a design, follow the same procedure in reverse. If you have access to a photocopier with an enlarging or reducing facility you can use this, which is a great time-saver.

Photocopying

Photocopying can be a good starting point for design. Make several photocopies of a subject – a drawing, a photograph, or an advertisement from a magazine, etc. These photocopies can be cut up and re-assembled, cut into strips and woven together, and 'played' with in all kinds of ways. The results can be pasted down, coloured, drawn on with crayons or pastels, or even photocopied themselves and again cut up and re-assembled, *ad infinitum*. There is no limit. Photocopies in which the images are not particularly clear often suggest textures or patterns which can be translated into stitchery.

Transferring a design on to canvas

This is quite a simple process. Place the design beneath the canvas and trace the main shapes on to the canvas with an indelible pen – a laundry marker is useful for this. If the shapes

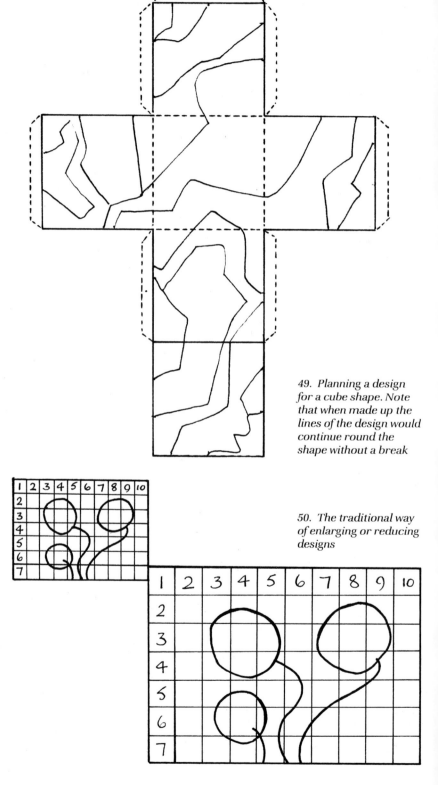

49. *Planning a design for a cube shape. Note that when made up the lines of the design would continue round the shape without a break*

50. *The traditional way of enlarging or reducing designs*

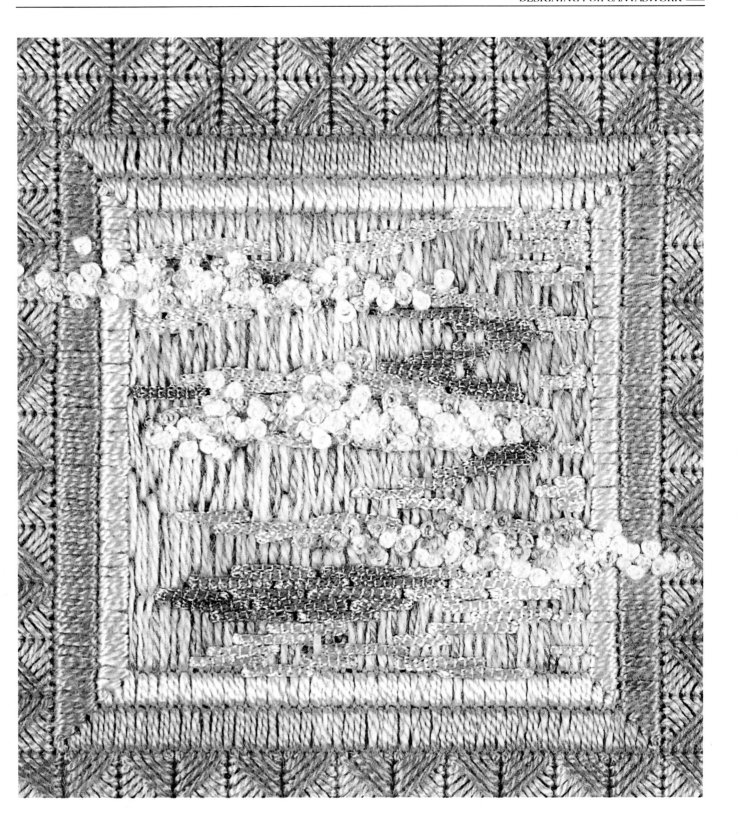

Small panel inspired by Monet's 'Water Lilies'. A wide
range of threads was used, both shiny and dull, and
including space-dyed tubular knitting yarn. Note how
the centre panel has been extended over the border
(Jaqui Bower)

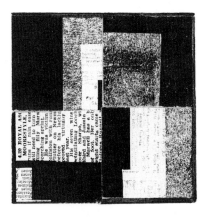

51. *Photocopies used as a design medium. (Top left) a paper collage based on a drawing. Note the use of tones. (Top right) Part of a photocopy has been cut into strips and reassembled. This could be turned into a rectangle, but left as it is it suggests an interesting shape for a banner. (Bottom left) A section of a photocopy has been cut up and rearranged. A design for a cushion or a rug perhaps? (Bottom right) Two photocopies were cut up and woven together. It looks rather 'busy' but by using a window viewer (i.e. a piece of card with a square or rectangle cut out of it, or two L-shapes) something usable might emerge which could be simplified*

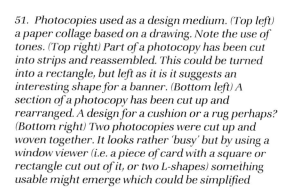

cannot be seen clearly it may be necessary to strengthen the outlines; to avoid marking the original drawing, take a tracing, strengthen the outlines with a black biro and place the tracing beneath the canvas instead of the original. If some details of the design are fiddly to transfer, simplify the shapes or try using a finer canvas. On the whole it is better to simplify rather than try to work on canvas a design which is not really suitable for this medium.

If you still have difficulty in seeing the design through the canvas, tape the design or tracing and canvas to a window; this should eliminate the problem.

Using graph paper to adapt a design to canvaswork

It sometimes happens that one wishes to adapt a drawing or design to canvaswork. As mentioned before, any design placed upon canvas will take on its geometric structure – the characteristic of canvaswork. The process of adaptation by means of graph paper is not difficult. Take a tracing of the design and transfer it on to the graph paper, then draw an outline round each shape, following the edges of the squares on the paper. Where there are curves or small details, 'step' the outline (as the curves in Florentine patterns are stepped) but keep as closely as possible to the original shape. If necessary, modify the original but, if a great deal of alteration is required, consider whether the design is really suitable for canvaswork.

Unless the gauge of the graph paper is the same as that of the canvas to be worked, the finished size will be larger or smaller than the original tracing, according to whether the graph paper or the canvas is the larger in scale. It may be wise to work a small area as a test piece; from this it will be possible to calculate the eventual size of the piece. If desired, the graph paper chart can be coloured to indicate where each coloured thread is used.

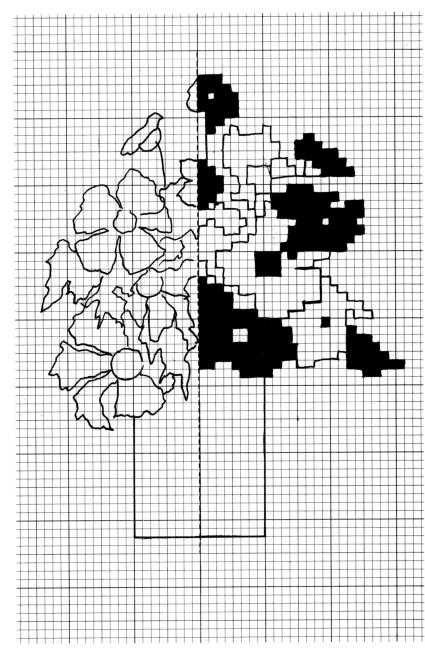

52. A drawing of flowers in a vase can be adapted for canvaswork by 'squaring-up' on graph paper. The procedure is described in the text

CHAPTER 7

CANVASWORK *for* PRACTICAL PURPOSES

Contemporary interest in embroidery tends towards the 'creative' – experimenting with fabrics, threads and mixed media to produce new ideas. At the same time, interest in making useful objects has waned, possibly because people today have less time to spare (canvaswork is a time-consuming exercise), materials are not cheap and there is a tempting variety of ready-made goods in the shops. However, there are still people who like,

and gain satisfaction from, using an article they have made themselves. Criticism is sometimes levelled at functional items because they look 'home-made', but there is no reason why they should do so if they are well-designed and suitable for their purpose.

It is important that functional items – garments, dress accessories, cushions, bags, etc. – are properly finished. After spending a considerable amount of time, effort and,

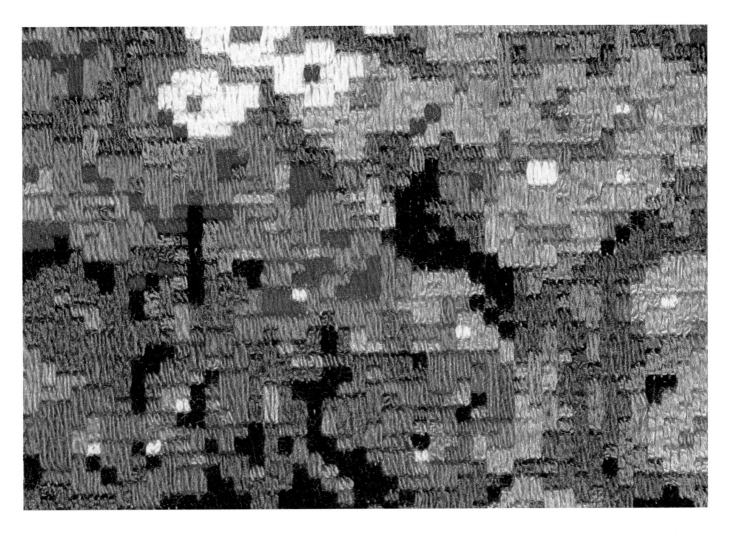

Detail of 'Herbaceous Border' (Vicky Lugg).
See page 59

53. *(Left) Small cushion or large pin-cushion worked*
on canvas. The background is in cross stitch using a
wool thread; details of the beadwork can be clearly
seen, and are typical of Victorian work
(Embroiderers' Guild Collection)

probably, money on a project, it is worth spending a little more to make a good job better. The finished work will look more professional and its life expectancy may well be increased. There are some excellent books available (most of them through public libraries) which are helpful in this respect.

Canvaswork combined with tweed, velvet, corduroy, denim, suede or leather looks well. If making up a three-dimensional piece presents problems, it may be worth considering whether a decorative panel of canvaswork applied to, or incorporated with, one of these materials would simplify matters. Always work one or two rows or stitches beyond the required size of the canvaswork so that no canvas is left showing at the seams when it is made up.

Some research may be necessary if the canvaswork is required to upholster a period chair or other piece of furniture. The style of the design should be appropriate to the age of the piece, and study of the colours used at the time of its production may be helpful. Books, museums, National Trust properties and stately homes are all useful for reference.

DECORATIVE PANELS AND WALL-HANGINGS

Panels and hangings provide opportunities to use materials and stitches in purely decorative ways, not suitable for wear and tear. Some suggestions are put forward in the chapter 'Experimental Canvaswork'. Large projects can be exciting and challenging. Sheer weight and size may present physical problems but these can be overcome with advance planning, sometimes by working a number of small pieces and assembling them into one larger piece. Hangings will probably need to be lined and possibly interlined as well.

BAGS AND PURSES

Bags and purses give tremendous scope for decoration, from a large, simple tote bag to the small, richly-embroidered flap of a purse. Scale of canvas and stitchery must be considered; very fine work could be used on a large bag, but coarse canvas and large stitches would be quite unsuitable for a small purse.

Again, finish is important. Bags are often better for a lining which should be made separately and inserted like an inner bag. An interlining of felt or plastic foam (although the

latter will eventually disintegrate) is also an improvement. Some bags or purses will be the better for the addition of a side gusset. Handles should be attached firmly and fastenings should also be secure.

CUSHIONS

Cushions range in size from pincushions to large floor cushions, and come in all shapes. The scale of the stitchery should look 'right' for the size of the cushion. Rug canvas would be quite suitable for a floor cushion, whereas a small pincushion needs a very fine canvas to avoid problems in making up. Geometric, stylized and formal designs are all suitable for decorating cushions which are seen from all angles; the size of the elements of the design should also be considered in relation to the size of the cushion. Choose stitches carefully: unless the cushion is purely for show and not for use, raised stitches will be subject to friction, causing them to wear out quickly. Long stitches may catch in things and should be avoided.

When making up cushions, the filling (which may be down, kapok, foam rubber chips, etc.) should be contained in an inner bag made from pre-shrunk strong fabric. The filling should be sufficient to make a firm cushion, but not so much as to make it uncomfortably hard. If feathers are used it should be made of a featherproof fabric. Ready-made cushion pads can be bought from department stores or specialist shops.

The appearance of cushions is very much improved if the seam round the edge is finished with a cord or piping. Instructions for making a piping can be found in books on soft furnishings and dressmaking.

LAMP BASES

Square, triangular, rectangular or cylindrical lamp bases look attractive covered with canvaswork, and can be related to the colour and design schemes of a room. The placing of the decoration should relate to the shape of the base; if necessary it must be planned to continue all round the base without a break. Strips or bands can be a simple solution to this.

The base on which the canvas is to be mounted should be solid and heavy, so that it cannot be knocked over easily. If hollow, the base can be filled with sand or pebbles to give stability. Bases for covering can be made from wood, plastic containers or found materials such as some kinds of pipes used by builders. The canvaswork for a cylindrical base can be made in one piece and joined with a single seam, making sure that the design/pattern joins up where it should. Square and other shapes with more than one side can also be made in one piece and wrapped round the shape or they can be made in four – or the appropriate number of – pieces and seamed at each angle. A curved needle makes this easier to do. It is sometimes possible to seam the canvaswork 'cover' and slip it over the base, but it may not give such a good fit. The top and foot of the base can be finished with a cord or braid if wished.

DOOR STOPS

These can be made by padding a brick with wadding, covering it with a strong cotton fabric, and making an outer 'skin' of canvaswork.

SMALL ITEMS

Spectacle cases, bookmarks, ecclesiastical burses and other small items are not onerous to undertake. If intended as a gift, the decoration can be given a personal slant; this will make the item particularly acceptable to the recipient. Again, the scale of the canvas and the design is important, and a very stiff canvas should be avoided if it is likely to present problems in making up. Details like linings and fastenings can also make or mar the finished piece.

GARMENTS

Any embroidery on clothes should form an integral part of the whole; it should not look as though it was put there as an afterthought. Embroidery should not be placed where it is likely to receive wear – where the sleeve rubs the side of a jacket, for instance.

Canvaswork is fairly stiff and is therefore not suitable for use on a draped garment or one that falls softly. Choose a garment pattern which avoids darts and gathers, and allow extra for seams if necessary. Simple ethnic shapes are good for decoration and an elementary knowledge of dressmaking is a great help.

Embroidery on garments is sometimes dismissed as 'arty-crafty' but this need not be so. If the decoration is discreet, well-placed and suitable for its purpose, a unique and very personal garment can result.

BELTS AND BUTTONS

As an alternative to using canvaswork on a garment, belts and buttons are worth considering. Before embarking on a belt, plan how it is to be fastened – the buckle or clasp may also suggest a design for the canvaswork. A belt will need to be interfaced to keep its shape, and it should also be lined; gloving leather or soft suede are good linings.

The finest possible canvas should be used for buttons. Ingenious embroiders will probably devise their own ways of making up buttons, but for speed and simplicity haberdashery departments carry ranges of metal and plastic button 'moulds' over which the canvas can be stretched and clipped in place. These come on cards, several in one size.

RUGS

Rug-making, particularly pile rugs, was a popular hobby some years ago. It was also a therapy for soldiers shell-shocked or wounded in World War I. Interest in these, and also in stitched rugs made with canvaswork stitches and rug yarn on coarse canvas, seems to have declined, but there is a great deal of scope in this area, not least for lively, original designs. Large-scale canvaswork is fairly quick to do and is suitable for people whose eyes may not allow them to do finer work. Flat, brick, gobelin, Florentine, long-armed cross and, of course, tent stitches all make good surfaces, and contrast can be introduced with velvet stitch, the loops of which can be cut or left uncut. For practical purposes, a rug in one colour exploiting contrasting textures works well. Simple arrangements of stripes or geometric patterns are also very successful, as can be seen from the durries and kelims now being imported in quantity.

All rugs need to be backed – traditionally with hessian. To prevent accidents, rugs should never be placed on a polished floor unless an additional non-slip backing is provided.

Decorative rugs can double as wall-hangings. These allow exciting colours and textures to be used, and alternative materials to traditional ones can be considered. At the other end of the scale, miniature rugs for dolls-houses (in line with current interest in these) are delightful, and can be interesting to research. They can also be mounted and framed.

Another type of stitched rug is based on the Arraiolos – the traditional needlework rugs of Portugal. Originally, the canvas used for these rugs resembled sacking or today's hessian and the patterns were based on Persian carpets and tiles, probably brought into Portugal by the Moors or later explorers. Local animals also feature in the designs. In early examples the designs are outlined in either stem or chain stitch, and then filled in with long-legged cross stitch, which sometimes follows the curves of the pattern but usually is worked back and forth across the canvas horizontally. There has been a revival of interest in these rugs and their traditional patterns, and there is a set procedure for making them.

First the edges of the canvas are oversewn and then hemmed. The hem is always turned *up* and in, not under; corners are mitred. The canvas is then marked with guidelines: double centre lines are drawn horizontally and vertically one stitch wide, so that the canvas is equally divided into four quarters; it is then marked out in 10-stitch blocks. The borders are marked with a double line, also one stitch wide.

The pattern is worked from the centre outwards, all outlines being worked first. The outlines are then filled in, and finally the background is worked. All stitching begins and ends on the right side, the ends being sewn under at least 5 stitches, and the back of the work should be as perfect as the front.

Long-armed cross stitch, worked vertically, horizontally, or diagonally as the design requires, is used throughout. The practice nowadays is to work smaller stitches over 2 × 4 threads and larger stitches over 3 × 6 threads. Earlier examples of this work show stitches over 1 × 2 threads.

BOXES

Canvaswork is very suitable for covering boxes, either on its own, combined with fabric, or set into the lid of a wooden box.

54. *Detail from a sampler, demonstrating the stages in the stitching of a Portuguese Arraiolos rug as described in the text. The background canvas can be seen, and also the long-legged (or long-armed) cross stitch work, horizontally, vertically and diagonally. The patterns are based on the traditional ones (Anne Woolston)*

Detail of 'Herbaceous Border' (Vicky Lugg).
See page 59

BOOK COVERS

Although book-binding skills are necessary for bound books, loose covers for books are comparatively simple to make and can be an interesting design project.

CHURCH KNEELERS

Kneeler schemes for local churches are proliferating all over the country. Kneelers receive hard wear, so it is essential to use the best materials within the budget – linen canvas and good quality crewel wools if possible. When designing for kneelers, remember that the top of the kneeler and, more particularly the centre, will receive the wear. Stitches should be selected for their hard-wearing qualities, bearing in mind that people should be able to kneel on them in comfort. Designs can reflect features of the church building, ecclesiastical symbols, life in the parish, landmarks of the neighbourhood, etc. Local flora and fauna may suggest designs, and geometrical patterns based on stitches, or taken from some decoration in the church itself, can be worked even by those with little experience. Simple ideas are often the most successful. If several designs are being used in one scheme, it is a good idea to link them together in some way, either by using variations on the arrangement of one group of colours throughout the scheme, or by repeating a particular motif in each kneeler. The kneelers at Guildford Cathedral are an example of the latter, where each kneeler's design is divided diagonally, representing the hill on which the cathedral stands.

Kneelers can be made up at home, but the job must be done with care so that the appearance of the finished kneelers is satisfactory and long-lasting. It may be better to consider having them made up professionally if there is doubt and funds are available.

COMMUNITY SCHEMES

Apart from kneelers, other groups may be involved in the production of commemorative hangings or panels for a particular situation, or as a gift to a public building such as a town hall or hospital. All such schemes will probably involve needlewomen of varying experience and, as with the kneeler schemes, canvaswork lends itself to all abilities.

Anything for public display must be worked to as high a design and technical standard as possible. The work needs to be guided along by a small 'committee' so that decisions can be taken and any complaints or recriminations do not fall on one pair of shoulders. If at all possible, recruit someone locally who has design experience and enlist his or her help, for if the design is not good, no amount of beautiful stitching will conceal it. It may also be necessary to arrange a few classes for the guidance of complete beginners, and those with limited experience of canvaswork, so that basic information on the use of frames, starting and finishing, etc. can be disseminated. The nearest branch of the Embroiderers' Guild may be able to offer assistance or advice. The address of the secretary may be obtainable from the public library or, failing that, it can be obtained from Embroiderers' Guild Headquarters at Hampton Court Palace, East Molesey, Surrey.

SIMPLE FINISHES

Fringes and tassels are sometimes needed with canvaswork and are quite easy to make. A tassel can be made with some of the threads used in the embroidery; tassels can be enriched with beads; bunches of small tassels can form larger tassels. Various ways of decorating the 'head' of a tassel can be invented, and a row of small tassels can form a fringe.

Fringes come in endless variety, from the simple one illustrated to the elaborate macramé fringes, instructions for which can be found in books on macramé and late Victorian needlework books and magazines.

Both tassels and fringes offer enormous scope for the imaginative use of all kinds of threads, fabrics and experimental materials. They can add the finishing touch, but before adding one or the other or both, consider whether it is practical and necessary.

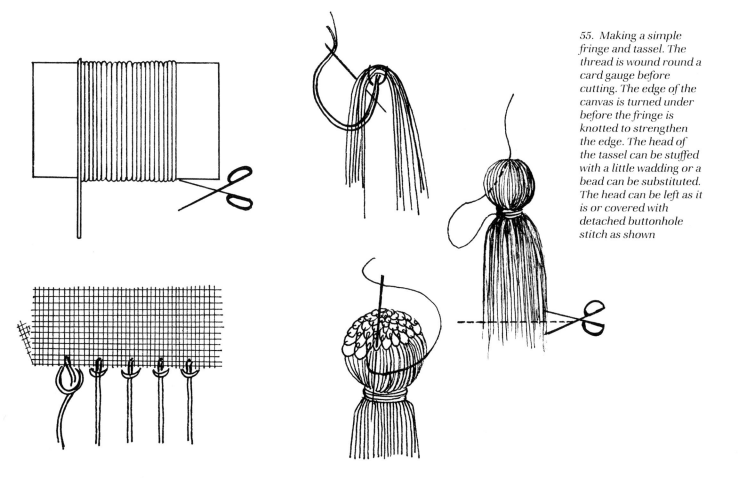

55. Making a simple fringe and tassel. The thread is wound round a card gauge before cutting. The edge of the canvas is turned under before the fringe is knotted to strengthen the edge. The head of the tassel can be stuffed with a little wadding or a bead can be substituted. The head can be left as it is or covered with detached buttonhole stitch as shown

CHAPTER 8

EXPERIMENTAL CANVASWORK

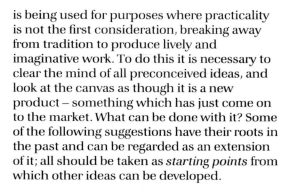

Ingenuity is a quality which should permeate the whole activity of embroidery ... It is something to be cultivated, controlled, and when necessary curbed. It is the power of ready invention, and can show itself in manual dexterity, in the lively use of materials, and in delight at seeing analogies and discerning possibilities.
  Kathleen White, Design in Embroidery

Canvaswork has proved its practical and hard-wearing qualities over the centuries. Today it

is being used for purposes where practicality is not the first consideration, breaking away from tradition to produce lively and imaginative work. To do this it is necessary to clear the mind of all preconceived ideas, and look at the canvas as though it is a new product – something which has just come on to the market. What can be done with it? Some of the following suggestions have their roots in the past and can be regarded as an extension of it; all should be taken as *starting points* from which other ideas can be developed.

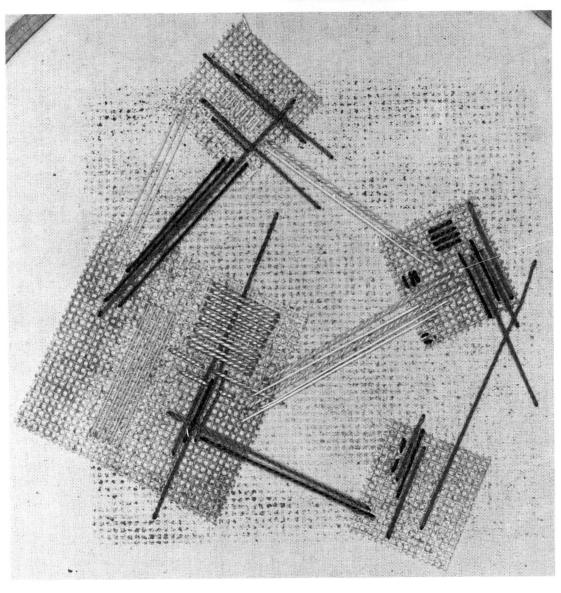

56. A piece of calico has been spray painted using a medium gauge canvas as a stencil. The canvas was then cut up and placed on the coloured background and stitches were added. This was a demonstration piece, but the idea could be taken much further (Margaret Rivers)

*Detail of a panel inspired by a garden and using torn
fabrics to create texture (Sheila Gussin)*

Paint, spray and dye

Painting a design on to canvas has long been practised – the printed canvas in kits shows you exactly where to place the various colours. The Victorians were able to buy black and coloured canvases, purple being especially popular. In experimental canvaswork, the background may be coloured wholly or in part, and may be allowed to show through the stitches as desired, or it may even be left unstitched to provide a contrast.

COLOURING THE CANVAS

Stretch a piece of canvas on a slate or rectangular frame, making sure that it is as taut as possible. The canvas can now be brushed with water-based paint, coloured inks, dye or fabric paints. At this stage the canvas will become limp; leave it to dry naturally (which may take some hours depending on the temperature of the room) and it will stiffen up again.

It is now ready for stitching, but be sure to work on a frame to avoid any distortion; the canvas cannot now be dampened for stretching, as this could make some of the colours run.

Further experiments can be made with acrylic paints, water-soluble crayons or pastels and other colouring agents. (N.B. It is possible that some colouring agents may fade or have a detrimental effect on the canvas and threads in time; many new products are untried in this respect, and it is too early for them to have proved themselves. Bear this in mind if the work is for sale. It is also important to read the manufacturer's instructions carefully in case they carry a warning of toxic fumes.)

Canvas can be sprayed with colour using a mouth diffuser or spray can. Drawing a knife along the bristles of an old toothbrush, which has been loaded with colour, also gives a fine spray. If the canvas is placed on a fabric background before spraying it will act as a stencil, and a pattern of small squares will be left on the fabric when the canvas is removed (be careful not to smudge it). Rug canvas is good for this. Pieces of canvas of different shapes can be moved around, sprayed again in another colour, or sprayed more deeply in some places than others. This creates an interesting background which can itself be stitched, and the coloured canvas can also be applied and stitched.

Spray painting can be rather messy, so protect the surrounding area with newspaper or a plastic sheet.

Changing the stitch

Canvas is an even-weave fabric. Canvaswork stitches, made by counting the threads, are regular. Stitches create texture; stitches make patterns; and changes of stitch direction give subtle colour changes. All these aspects of stitches can be exploited and interpreted anew.

Many stitches traditionally associated with surface stitchery can be adapted to canvas. Changing the thickness of the thread may be all that is needed to give a stitch an entirely new dimension. Composite stitches worked on a 'ladder' can be translated into canvaswork by omitting the ladder and working the second journey of the stitch directly on to the canvas, e.g. **raised chain band**.

Stitches can be worked freely, can be distorted, and can be worked on top of one another. **Herringbone** and **cretan stitches** lend themselves to these treatments.

Back stitch worked diagonally on canvas, gives a very solid, firm fabric. The appearance is similar to tent stitch but with the added advantage that, if parts of the design are also worked directionally, e.g. in chevron patterns, subtle colour changes will occur due to the play of light. Worked vertically and/or horizontally, some interesting effects can be made with back stitch.

Running stitch worked on canvas has a more open appearance than back stitch. It too can be worked directionally, so that the play of light will produce variations of tone. Lines or areas of running stitch contrast well with more solid areas of stitchery.

Long straight stitches – particularly if used on a painted canvas which shows through the stitches – have great possibilities. Patterns can be built up with them; stitch direction can suggest three dimensions; stitches can be layered; thicker and thinner threads can contrast; random-dyed threads give unexpected colour changes.

57. This unusual texture was made by crocheting into a piece of large-gauge canvas and then filling in with tent stitch (Phoebe Kane)

Darning or weaving on canvas is really an extension of running stitch. Stitches can be spaced and the length changed to form patterns; surfaces can be varied by changing the thread or the colour, or by embellishing with further stitchery.

Crocheting into canvas produces an interesting textured surface.

Couching

Thick or knobbly threads will not pass through the canvas themselves, but can be used by means of couching them on the surface, i.e. the thread lies on the surface, and is tied down by means of a thinner and smoother thread which can be passed through the canvas. Couched threads can lay directly on the canvas or over an area of other stitches. They can be stitched down in patterns – something like the *or nué* technique in metal thread work. Couched threads can form curves.

Romanian and Bokhara couching might be adapted to canvaswork, and experiments could be made with underside couching, where the tying-down thread actually pulls a loop of the couched thread through to the back of the work.

Knotted threads and braids can be couched, and although not strictly couching, perhaps, wrapped threads, string, cocktail sticks, dowelling, drinking straws, etc. can all be attached to a canvas background by means of stitches. Here, again, the attaching stitches can form patterns and the wrapped threads, etc., can be placed close together or spaced out. The canvas can be stitched first to make a background for the attached pieces, or it can be left unworked and stitched later. Innumerable ways of attaching things can be devised.

Cocktail sticks, drinking straws, etc., will need to be wrapped by hand, but threads and narrow cords can be covered with a close machine zigzag stitch. Some sewing machines have an embroidery foot, through which a thread can be passed and held in position for covering. Pieces of fabric cut on the bias can be rolled and couched down with a matching or contrasting thread. Printed silk and metallic fabrics are particularly effective used in this way.

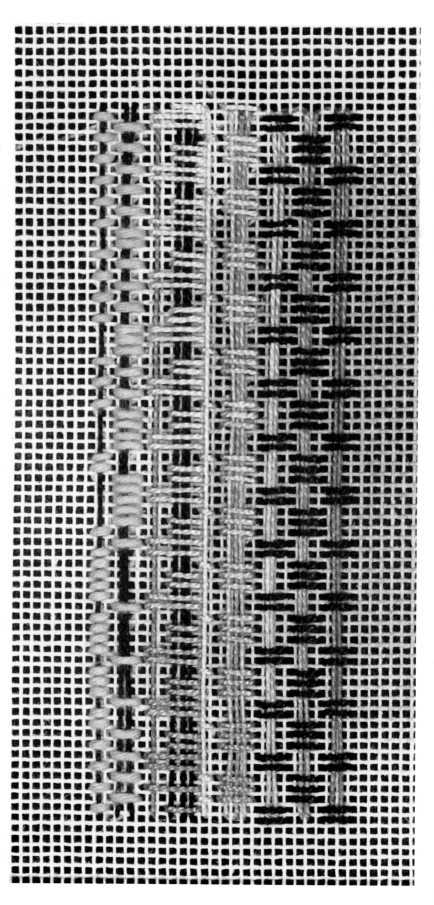

58. Threads have been couched on to a painted background and the couching stitches arranged in regular patterns. The stitches need not be spaced so evenly and there is a great deal of scope here for couching cords, ribbons, etc (Margaret Rivers)

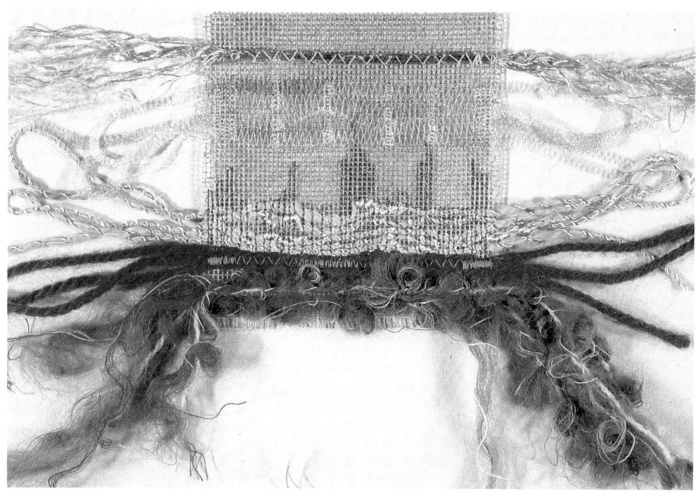

Painted canvas sample with applied and machine-
couched threads, including tubular knitting yarn
(Lesley Barnett)

Changing the surface

Ideas can be culled from traditional embroidery methods such as **pulled work** and **drawn thread work**. Interlocked canvas (identified by the twisted threads where warp and weft cross) is not suitable for these experiments, but the threads of loosely woven canvas can be worked with pulled work stitches to create lacy patterns. The linking thread between stitches, usually concealed at the back of the work, may show through the more open canvas, but could be made a feature of the patterns.

The drawn thread technique can also be adapted to canvaswork. Threads are withdrawn either horizontally and/or vertically. The remaining threads can then be needlewoven, bunched together, or interlaced as in conventional drawn thread work. Needlewoven threads can be further embellished with beads, bugles, ribbons or additional looped threads. Small tassels could even be tied on. Any remaining area of canvas might be solidly stitched as a contrast to the open areas of drawn thread. Openwork can be thrown into relief by backing it with a contrasting colour, or possibly with more canvaswork.

Using coloured canvas and brightly coloured or metallic threads, rich surfaces can be created by these methods. They are not necessarily ends in themselves, but might form elements in larger compositions of fabric and thread.

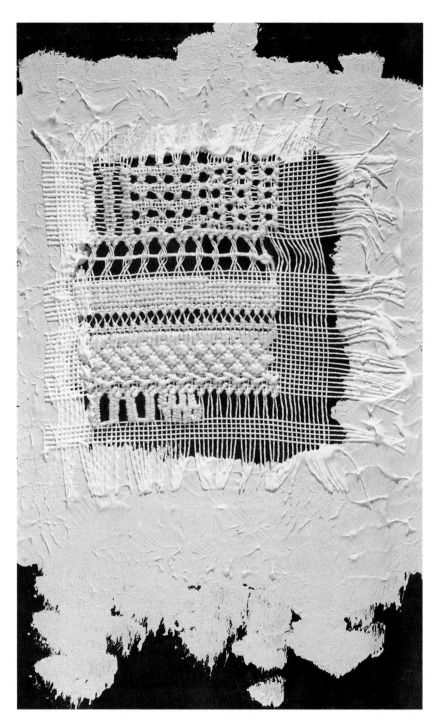

59. *Threads were withdrawn from this loosely-woven canvas; those remaining were then worked with pulled and drawn thread stitches, and a little needleweaving, plus some tent and herringbone stitches, with some double cross stitches made with a small diagonal cross on top of a larger straight cross. As a further experiment the sample was then mounted on a piece of board by thickly applying acrylic paint (Margaret Rivers)*

Manipulating canvas

If canvas (particularly non-interlocking canvas) is dampened with water, or moistened with PVA adhesive, it can be manipulated, pulled out of shape or even moulded over a form such as a wooden bowl. In the case of the latter, the form can be protected by covering it with baking parchment before the canvas is moulded round it. Shaped canvas can be sprayed with colour or painted; or it can be stitched. Stitches worked after the canvas has been pulled out of shape will themselves be distorted. Threads can also be stretched across three-dimensional forms.

Manipulated canvas usually looks better if canvas and threads are kept to one colour, or tones of one colour. A variation on this is to spray the whole thing with metallic paint when the work is finished, which can be very effective.

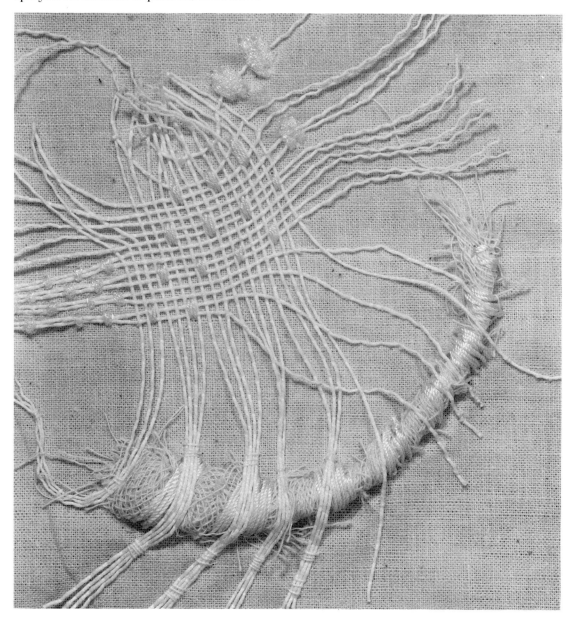

60. A scrap of canvas was moistened and partly unravelled; it was then stitched to a calico background and some of the ends taken over a roll of partly-wrapped scrim (Margaret Rivers)

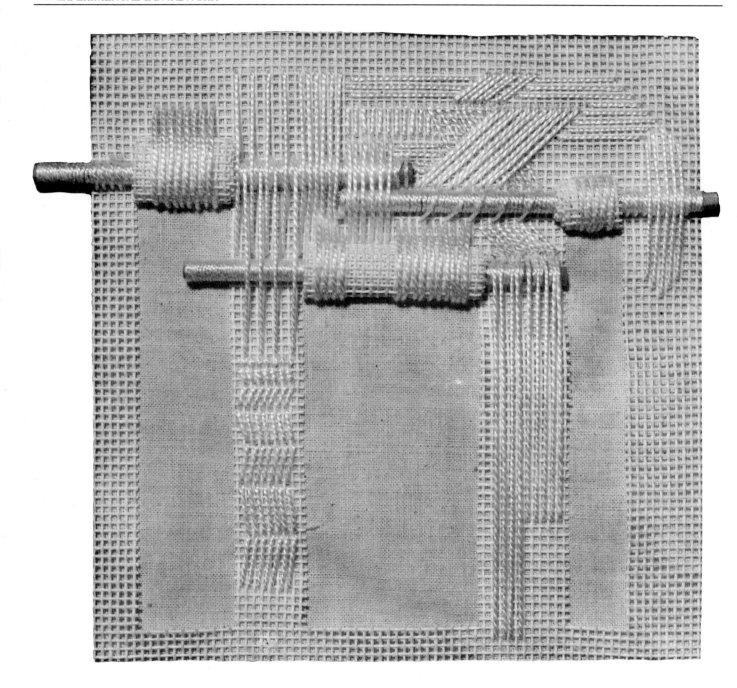

Cutting

Interlocked canvas can be cut without fear that it will unravel, although there may be times when loose threads can be incorporated into a design. A regular pattern of cuts in the canvas can have threads or strips of fabric threaded through them, or parts of the canvas can be turned back to reveal something underneath. Irregularly shaped holes can also be made. To make sure that edges will remain firm, a touch of PVA adhesive can be applied to them.

Canvas shapes, such as leaves or petals, can be cut out and, again, PVA adhesive, touched to the edges, will secure any tendency to unravel. If wire (fuse wire or millinery wire) is overcast to the edges, the shape can be bent and manipulated. The canvas can be stitched and edges can be overcast if necessary. Such shapes can either be applied to a background or assembled into three-dimensional objects.

61. Cuts were made in the canvas and the resulting strips rolled over wrapped dowelling, making raised areas over which long threads were stretched. It would be better to use interlocked canvas for this sort of experiment. It could also be worked on a much larger scale (Margaret Rivers)

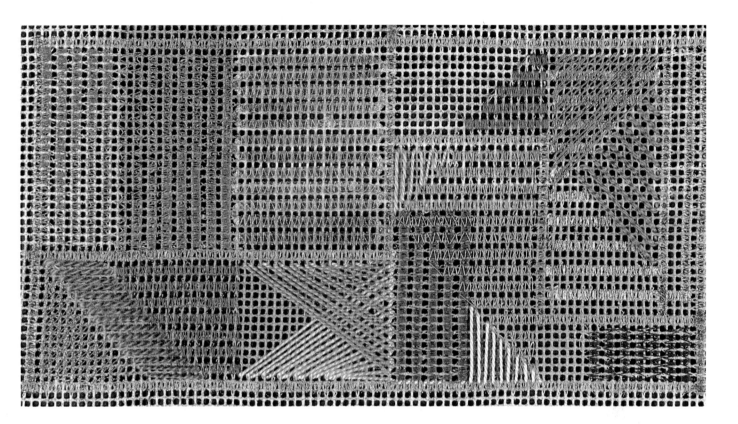

*Experimental canvaswork. Painted canvas with
machine and hand stitching in a variety of threads
(Lesley Barnett)*

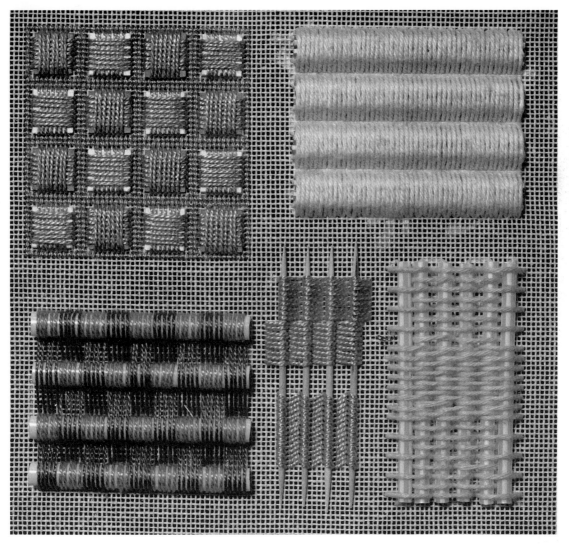

62. Card, cocktail sticks and plastic drinking straws have been lightly stitched to the canvas and then covered with further stitching to make raised surfaces. This could be effective if carried out on a background of canvaswork (Margaret Rivers)

Raising the surface

Prepared canvases, sold commercially, are sometimes covered with long horizontal stitches, indicating where the colours of the design should be placed. These canvases are described as 'trammed' and the process as 'tramming'. Double thread (or Penelope) canvas is generally used and the horizontal threads are laid between the double threads. The effect is to raise slightly the half cross or gobelin stitch worked over the laid thread, and after several rows have been worked it gives a corded appearance. By increasing the thickness of the laid thread the effect will be exaggerated. Other stitches, for example, cross stitch or oblong cross stitch, can be raised by padding them with a laid thread. Cocktail sticks, string (which can be coloured), plastic drinking straws, metal rods, etc., can be substituted for the laid thread and have stitches worked over them.

A stitched canvas which is flexible enough can be quilted, either by making a 'sandwich' of a backing, wadding and the worked canvas, and stitching through all three layers, or by stuffing from the back isolated areas, which have previously been backed with fabric and outlined with stitches; the backing fabric is slashed, wadding is inserted as necessary, and the slit is sewn up again. This is the Trapunto method of quilting.

Lengths of wooden dowel, pieces of card or balsa wood can be coloured or wrapped with thread, or fabric strips cut on the bias, and secured to a canvas background, either before or after it is stitched, depending on the required effect. Long stitches can be passed over the raised areas to give an undulating surface, perhaps continuing into conventional canvaswork stitches by way of contrast. The securing stitches could be worked in some sort of pattern.

Changing the scale

Stitches worked over varying numbers of threads are one way of changing scale, but some stitches do not easily adapt to this; others may need a change in the thickness of the thread to be satisfactory.

A partly-worked eighteenth-century chair back, in the Embroiderers' Guild Collection, has the faces and hands of the figures worked separately in tent stitch on a fine linen, and then cut out and applied to the background of coarser linen; the joins are concealed by the larger-scale tent stitches of the background, which are taken over them.

A similar effect can be achieved by using double thread canvas. The threads can be manipulated with a needle to make a single thread area where required. The term for this process is 'pricking the ground'. The fine stitches worked on the single thread will contrast with the larger stitches worked on the double thread. Some examples of this method are worked with tent stitch on the single threads and cross stitch on the double threads.

Today's embroiderers, many of whom have little time to spare, may find 'pricking the ground' tedious. An alternative is to lay a piece of finer canvas on top of a coarser one (or *vice versa*), the stitches then being taken through both layers. This method works well if the holes coincide comfortably. If not, the solution may be to cut a hole in the background canvas and lay the other one behind or in front of it. If an interlocking canvas is used as background there should be no problem with fraying. The edges of the hole will be covered by the stitching.

63. Detail from a partly-worked eighteenth-century chair cover. The hands, face and hair are worked on a finer linen than the main background and then applied. Tent stitch is used throughout, but the two gauges of linen change the scale of the stitch (Embroiderers' Guild Collection)

Machining on canvas

Quite a different approach to canvaswork can be made through the sewing machine. By using the satin (zigzag) stitch, the mesh of the canvas can be completely covered with thread. This is particularly effective if a metallic or random thread is used. Parts of the covered mesh can then be worked with stitches in the usual way, or further machine embroidery can be added – some areas closely covered with texture, others left open. Alternatively hand and machine stitchery can be combined.

On large gauge canvases, such as rug canvas, a grid of fine machine straight stitching can be superimposed on the grid of the canvas, giving contrast and inviting further experiment.

64. (Right) Canvas covered with machine satin stitch can then be over-stitched by hand or, if rug canvas is used, machine straight stitch freely worked, can be taken across the canvas to form lacy fillings. There are many more possibilities (Margaret Rivers)

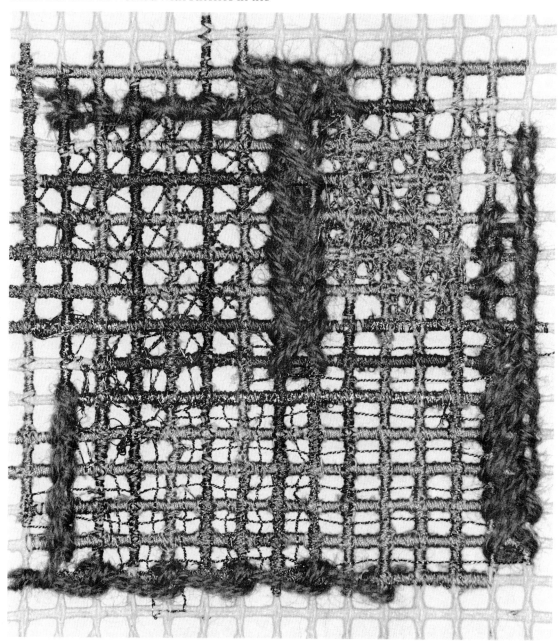

(Left) Unfinished experimental piece by Jenifer Murray. The canvas was painted metallic gold; hand-made paper flower shapes were applied and covered with a layer of organza. More stitchery has yet to be worked

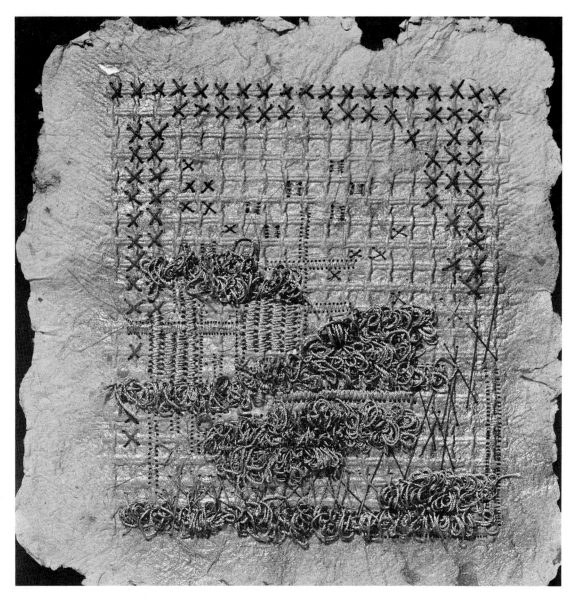

65. Rug canvas was embedded in home-made paper pulp and left to dry. Experiments were then made with hand and machine stitching (Margaret Rivers)

Mixed media

Using more than one embroidery technique in a piece of work has become acceptable, and for some time now *avant garde* artists in textiles have combined stitchery with paper, felt, paint, plastics, wood and other unexpected media. This trend presents many opportunities to the adventurous canvasworker.

Paper. Specialist shops now stock a wide range of hand- and machine-made papers. Some Japanese papers have a regular pattern of holes which suggest experiments with canvaswork stitches; the paper needs to be supported by a fabric background and the stitches taken through both. This paper can also be darned. Paper made at home can include canvas embedded in the pulp; when dry this can be worked further. Very thin paper, such as tissue paper or lens tissue, can be laid over canvas and stitches taken through both, using the canvas as a guide. If the paper is thin enough it will be possible to see the mesh of the canvas through it but, if not, prick the paper from the reverse side to indicate where the needle should penetrate before beginning to stitch. Paper strips can be woven into rug canvas and, if the paper is tough enough to stand it, hand or machine stitchery can be added to the resulting surface.

The Yellow Pages and advertisements in craft magazines will help to locate suppliers of Japanese and other interesting papers, some of whom offer a mail order service.

Felt. The current interest in hand-made felt can be utilized in canvaswork. Strands of fleece can be woven or darned into canvas to form a surface for further stitchery by hand or machine. Strips of commercial felt can also be darned into canvas. Rug canvas machined on to thick, soft felt makes an interesting regular texture, as the felt pushes up through the holes of the canvas in little 'cushions'. Canvaswork inlay with felt looks most effective and some beautiful work has been produced in this way, notably by Joanne Satchell.

Plastic and **wood** combined with or on canvas might inspire yet other new approaches.

66. Tent stitch worked on canvas was inlaid into a piece of hand-made felt in this sample by Joanne Satchell. The felt was stab stitched for contrasting texture (Embroiderers' Guild Collection)

FURTHER READING

NOTE: Some of the books listed here are now out of print, but should be obtainable by special request through the public library service.

Chapter 1

CAULFIELD & SAWARD, *Encyclopedia of Victorian Needlework*, Dover, 1972 (see 'Berlin Work' for description of plush stitch)

DIGBY, George Wingfield, *Elizabethan Embroidery*, Faber, 1963

EDWARDS, Joan, *Small Books on the History of Embroidery – Berlin Work*, Bayford Books, 1980

HOGARTH, Mary, *Modern Embroidery*, Studio Publications, 1933

HUMPHREY, Carol, 'Canvaswork' in *The Royal School of Needlework Book of Needlework and Embroidery*, ed. L. Synge, Collins, 1986

KENDRICK, A. F., *English Needlework*, A & C Black, 1967

LEVEY, Santina, *Discovering Embroidery of the 19th Century*, Shire Publications, 1971

PROCTOR, Molly, *Victorian Canvaswork*, Batsford, 1972, 1986

SNOOK, Barbara, *English Embroidery*, Batsford, 1960

SWAIN, Margaret, *The Needlework of Mary, Queen of Scots*, Van Nostrand Reinhold, 1973

Chapter 2

ERLANDSEN & MOOI, *The Bead Book: Sewing and Weaving with Beads*, Van Nostrand Reinhold

NORDFORS, Jill, *Needlelace and Needleweaving*, Studio Vista, 1974

Chapter 3

GRAY, Jennifer, *Canvaswork*, Batsford

GREEN, Sylvia, *Canvas Embroidery for Beginners*, Studio Vista, 1970

THOMAS, Mary, *Mary Thomas's Embroidery Book*, Hodder & Stoughton, 1936

Chapter 4

HUGGINS, Mabel & BLAKEY, Clarice, *Stitches on Canvas*, Batsford, 1988

RHODES, Mary, *Dictionary of Canvaswork Stitches*, Batsford, 1980, 1989

SNOOK, Barbara, *Embroidery Stitches*, Batsford, 1963

THOMAS, Mary, *Mary Thomas's Dictionary of Embroidery Stitches*, Hodder & Stoughton, 1934

Chapter 5

ALLEN, Jeanne, *The Designer's Guide to Japanese Patterns*, Thames & Hudson, 1988

BAIN, George, *Celtic Art, The Methods of Construction*, Constable, 1951

CHRISTIE, Archibald H, *Pattern Design*, Dover, 1969

CRITCHLOW, Keith, *Islamic Patterns, An Analytical and Cosmological Approach*, Schocken Books, 1976

DYE, Daniel Sheets, *The New Book of Chinese Lattice Designs*, Dover, 1981

JONES, Diana, *Patterns for Canvas Embroidery*, Batsford, 1977

LANTZ, Sherlee *A Pageant of Pattern for Needlepoint Canvas*, André Deutsch, 1974

LANTZ, Sherlee, *Trianglepoint from Persian Pavilions to Op Art with One Stitch*, Viking Press (New York), 1976

PROCTOR, Richard M, *The Principles of Pattern for Craftsmen and Designers*, Van Nostrand Reinhold, 1969

SLADE, Richard, *Geometrical Patterns*, Faber and Faber 1970

SNOOK, Barbara, *Florentine Embroidery*, Charles Scribner, 1967

Chapter 6

BEST, Muriel & LUGG, Vicky, *Design Sources for Embroidery*, Batsford, 1988

EMBROIDERERS' GUILD PRACTICAL STUDY GROUP, *Needlework School*, Windward Press, 1984

GORDON, Maggie, *Alphabets and Images, Inspiration from Letter Forms*, Batsford, 1974

HOWARD, Constance, *Embroidery & Colour*, Batsford, 1976

RUSSELL, Pat, *Lettering for Embroidery*, Batsford, 1980

SPRINGALL, Diana, *Canvas Embroidery*, Batsford, 1980

Chapter 7

DE DILLMONT, Thérèse, *The Complete Encyclopedia of Needlework*, (see entry for Fringes and Tassels)

EDWARDS, Joan, *Picture Book for Kneeler Makers*, Bayford Books

LEMON, Jane, *Embroidered Boxes and other Construction Techniques*, Batsford, 1984, 1986

MATHEWS, Sybil I, *Needlemade Rugs*, Mills & Boon

MONTAGU, Belinda, *Group Work in Embroidery*, Batsford, 1986

RHODES, Mary, *Needlepoint: The Art of Canvas Embroidery*, Octopus

STONE, Patricia, *Portuguese Needlework Rugs*, EPM Publications (USA)

THOMSON, Barbara & TREWIN, Wendy, *Embroidered Church Kneelers*, Batsford, 1987

ZNAMIEROWSKI, Nell, *Rugmaking*, Pan Craft Books

Chapter 8

EVERS, Inge, *Feltmaking Techniques and Projects*, A & C Black, 1987

FREW, Hannah, *Three-dimensional embroidery*, Van Nostrand Reinhold (see 'Construction Methods'), 1975

SHANNON, Faith, *Paper Pleasures*, Mitchell Beazley, 1987

SUPPLIERS

Frames, canvas, threads, beads, etc.

Barnyarns
Langrish
Petersfield
Hampshire GU32 1RQ

The Campden Needlecraft Centre
High Street
Chipping Campden
Gloucestershire

The Handworker's Market
18 Chapel Yard
Albert Street
Holt
Norfolk

John Lewis PLC
Oxford Street
London W1

Liberty & Co
Regent Street
London W1

Mace & Nairn
89 Crane Street
Salisbury
Wiltshire SP1 2PY

Maple Textiles
188–190 Maple Road
Penge
London SE20 8HT

Needle & Thread
80 High Street
Horsell
Woking
Surrey

Christine Riley
53 Barclay Street
Stonehaven
Kincardineshire AB3 2AR

Threadbare
Glenfield Park
Glenfield Road
Nelson
Lancashire

Tri-Thy Craft & Needlework Centre
Coed Talon
Near Mold
Clwyd CH7 4TU

Rug and rya canvas

Royal Wilton Carpet Factory
Wilton, Near Salisbury
Wiltshire

Leather, gold and silver kid

A L Maugham & Co Ltd
5–9 Fazakerley Street
Liverpool L3 9DN

Dyes, art and craft material

L Cornelissen & Son Ltd
105 Great Russell Street
London WC1

Frank Herring & Son
27 High West Street
Dorchester
Dorset DT7 10P

Reeves Dryad Ltd
178 Kensington High Street
London W8

INDEX

alphabets 64
Arraiolos rugs 37, 74
Aston Hall, Birmingham 8

Bargello *see* Florentine
beading needles 25
beadwork
    grisaille 9
    raised 26
    Victorian 9, 10
Berlin woolwork 9, 55, 58
Bess of Hardwick 8
Booker, Aileen 11

canvas
    braiding 10
    double thread (Penelope) 13,
        15
    interlocked 12, 13, 15, 84
    plastic 19
    pricking 89
    raffia 13
    rug 13, 15, 22, 36
    Rya 13, 15, 16
    silk gauze 13
    single (mono) 13, 15
    waste 13, 15
    Winchester 19
card mounts 30
carpets 8
Celtic ornament 55
Chester Town Hall 9
chicken wire 19
China, canvaswork on silk
    gauze 17
City & Guilds embroidery
    courses 11
congress work 10
corners, turning 46
couching 19, 25, 43, 45, 82
crewel wool 19
crochet 80–81
curved needles 13
cushions 8, 72

darning 81, 92
direction
    cross stitch 37
    play of light 42
    stitch 36, 64
distortion 12
drawn thread 84
dyes, chemical 9

eighteenth century 8–9
Embroiderers' Guild 6, 9, 11

fabric, torn 19
felt
    as interlining 72
    canvaswork inlay 93
    for mounting 30
    strips 19
finishing 70–2
flame stitch *see* Florentine

Flight, Claude 11
Florentine
    four-sided 53, 54
    'free' 55
    historical 7, 9
    stitch 12, 52–3
fringes 76–7
furniture
    bed 8
    upholstered 9, 52, 72

garments 73
gauze 13, 17, 19
glazing 30
graph paper
    isometric 46
    patterns, planning 46
grids 46, 49, 50
grisaille 9

hangings
    bed 8
    Hatton Garden 8
    historical 7
    Lady Mary Holte 8–9
hassocks *see* kneelers
Hogarth, Mary 11
Hungarian point *see* Florentine

interlaced patterns 57
interlining
    bags 72
    belts 73
    hangings 33, 72
interlocked canvas 12, 13, 15, 84
isometric graph paper 46
ivory work 10

leather 19, 33
leno 13
linen
    even-weave 7
    scrim 19
lining
    bags 72
    belts 73
    panels and hangings 32, 33,
        72
lockweave 13

Mary Queen of Scots 8
mathematical progressions 50
metal
    mesh 15, 19, 20
    threads 19
mono canvas 13
monograms 64
Morris, William 9

needleweaving 84
net 15, 19
nineteenth century 9–10
nylon mesh 15

padding 33

paper 92
paste 9
Penelope canvas 13
picture stretchers 12
Pincus, Helen 19, 20
pincushions 8, 72
plastic
    canvas 19, 20
    foam, as interlining 72
    foam, for mounting 30
    mesh 19
plushwork 9, 10
Portuguese rugs 37, 74
pricking the ground 89
pulled work 84

quilting 88

raffia
    canvas 13
    synthetic 20
    thread 19, 22
Rhodes, Mary 45
ribbons 19, 24, 43
rubbings 64
rug canvas 13, 15, 22, 36
rugs 73–4
rya canvas 13, 15, 16

scale
    contrasting 35
    stitches 36, 89
scrim 19
Second World War 11
sequins 25
seventeenth century 8
silk
    gauze 13, 17
    threads 19
    torn, as an alternative
        thread 19
single thread canvas 13, 15
sixteenth century 8
slate frame 12
slips 8
spangles 25
stiches
    Algerian eye 45
    back 80
    brick 40, 41, 73
    buttonhole 45
    Byzantine 40, 41
    chain 42, 45, 74
    changing 80
    chequer 44, 46
    contrasting textures 36
    couching 36, 45
    cretan 80
    cross 7, 36–8, 88
    direction 36, 64
    double cross (Smyrna) 36, 37,
        38
    eye 45
    fern 42
    fishbone 42

flat (mosaic, cushion) 27, 40,
        41, 46, 73
    Florentine (flame) 52–3, 73
    fly 45
    French knots 8
    gobelin 40, 41, 73, 88
    half cross 37, 38, 88
    herringbone 36, 80
    jacquard 44
    knots 45
    long-armed (long-legged)
        cross 37, 38, 73, 74
    oblong cross 37, 38, 88
    Parisian 40, 41
    patterns with 36
    plush 9
    raised chain band 36, 80
    raising 45
    ray 42
    reverse tent 37
    reversed cross 37, 38
    Rhodes 45
    rice 8, 27, 36, 38, 40
    rococo 8
    running 80
    Scottish 44, 46
    star 45
    stem 74
    straight cross 37, 38
    straight or satin 40, 41, 80
    tent 7–8, 26, 36–7, 39, 73
    upright cross 37
    velvet 9, 39, 73
    web 42
stretchers, picture 12
stretching 29, 30
string 19
superimposing 45

tambour frame 12
tapestry needles 13
tapestry wool 19
tassels 76–7
tension 12, 19
texture
    as part of design 64
    pattern 46
    stitches 36
threads, random-dyed 80
three-dimensional items, making
    up 72
tramming 13, 37, 88
Trapunto quilting 88
triangles 46
'Tumbling Blocks' 55
twentieth century 11

Victoria and Albert Museum 6, 8

waste canvas 13, 15
weaving 81
Willis, Rosamund 11
Winchester canvas 19
wood 92, 93
wrapping 82